The Wonderful World

Th

Shadow Relief Maps by Geographical Projects
Under the direction of Shirley Carpenter
Developed from a new method invented by
Professor Frank Debenham

Isotypes by Isotype Institute
Under the direction of Marie Neurath
These are simple visual explanations created in
a skilfully developed picture language

Art by Kempster and Evans
The paintings sum up and interpret the story
with emotional impact and scientific accuracy

Part I

Part II

Part III

Wonderful World

THE ADVENTURE OF THE EARTH WE LIVE ON

How the World Began

The World in the Making
The Four Ages of Life
Man's Age of Life

The Face of the World

The Earth and the Sun
The Winds Blow
Nature's Work

Man's World

How Man Lives
Where Man Lives
Man and his Faiths
Man and the Unknown
The Last Secrets

by **JAMES FISHER**

Art Editor : **F.H.K.HENRION**

HANOVER HOUSE   GARDEN CITY   NEW YORK

FIRST PUBLISHED IN THE UNITED STATES OF AMERICA 1954

PLUTO

NEPTUNE

URANUS

JUPITER

PLANETOIDS

MARS

VENUS

EARTH

I
How The World Began

WE who live on earth have been thinking about the Universe, and its stars and planets, for only a few thousand years; and making observations with elaborate scientific equipment for a few hundred. So we know very little about it, except that there are great mysteries yet to be explored and explained.

Where, or what, did our sun and its system come from? How did nine planets come to travel round the sun in orbits arranged in a plane or disc? How did Life arise on at least one planet, Earth, and probably another, Mars?

THE WORLD IN THE MAKING

Nobody knows for certain how the solar system began—how the sun came to have nine planets, with their moons and rings, and thousands of tiny planetoids. Some scientists think that about 2,500 million years ago the sun and a greater star revolved round each other. Astronomers know many such 'double stars' in the Universe. Suddenly the greater star exploded; most of its material rushed to another part of the galaxy of stars to which our sun belongs: but it left behind a disc of gas and other matter which remained attracted by, and revolving round, the sun. This stuff soon gathered into four or five masses.

According to this theory, the big masses later split into unequal parts, of which the largest became the giant planets Jupiter, Saturn, Uranus, and Neptune. The smallest, Uranus, is 30 thousand miles across; the largest, Jupiter, 90 thousand. The five other chief planets are Mercury, Venus, Earth, Mars and Pluto, and these are all between three and eight thousand miles across. Earth, the largest of these, has a diameter of 7,900 miles. Most of the planetoids may be the remains of a broken-up planet between Mars and Jupiter; the largest of them is Ceres, 480 miles across.

Moons orbit round planets, not the sun. We do not know whether Pluto has any, and we know Mercury and Venus have not: all the other planets have at least one moon. Both Jupiter and Saturn have moons bigger than the planet Mercury. Neptune has one about as big. Jupiter has, besides, two moons about the size of Earth's single moon, which is 2,160 miles across. As well as nine moons, Saturn has rings, which may be ice particles. The smaller of Mars' two tiny moons is only five miles across.

All together, the planets total no more than a seven-hundredth of the mass of the sun and now shine only in its reflected light. Several of them, and several moons, have atmospheres of gas—water-vapour, carbon dioxide, air, methane or ammonia; but the only ones that can support life as we know it are Earth, probably Mars and possibly Venus. On one side of Mercury the temperature would melt lead and is too hot for life; on the other, which never sees the sun, it is too cold. On the rest of the planets the temperature is too low and any atmosphere may be poisonous. In proportion to its size, Earth is the heaviest of the planets; it contains huge amounts of iron. So far, man has penetrated only a few miles into its crust, and knows very little about its inside. Scientists disagree about the size of the earth's innermost core; whether it is liquid rock or iron and whether it is hot or cool. But most of them think that the earth has had much the same sort of crust and temperature for at least 1,000 million years. During this time it has shrunk a little, which has caused the crust to buckle and fold, forming mountains.

Compared with the life-span of a living thing, the span of geological time is vast. The longest-lived plants seem to die when they are about 4,000 years old, and no animal lives longer than about a hundred and fifty years. Yet it is perhaps 1,000 million years since life began on Earth, probably in the shallow edge of a warm sea. It could not have begun without water, air and the element carbon.

Living things can make complicated substances out of simple ones; they grow and reproduce themselves in a way that lifeless matter cannot do. No two succeeding generations of any kind of living thing are ever exactly the same. We call this change, which goes on from generation to generation, evolution. What evolution has done lies all around us. Several million different sorts of animals and plants now share the world with man; all are probably descended from the first simple living substances of earth. Before we see how living things inherited the earth, we must understand something about the rocks of the earth's crust. There are two main kinds, igneous and sedimentary.

Igneous rocks (meaning rocks associated with fire) come from hot parts of the earth's crust, or possibly from below it. They penetrate, as liquids, along lines of weakness in the crust and may appear at the surface or form masses of rock under it.

Sedimentary rocks (rocks which are laid down) are formed as the result of erosion – eating away. Existing surface rocks, sedimentary or igneous, are constantly subjected to erosion by wind, frost, ice, water, or sand. The material worn away becomes mud or sand. This finds its level and settles in horizontal, or nearly horizontal beds, at the bottom of seas, lakes and basins: or it blows across the land into dunes and banks.

We can date the strata by the remains of living things in them. The fossil record tells us nearly all we know about life in the past. But it did not begin until about 500 million years ago, when living things had hard parts their — skeletons — to leave behind after death.

Some parts of the earth's crust are very much hotter than others, probably owing to energy given off by the slow changing of some substances into others. We call this radioactivity. Rock which is melted by this heat, can be forced to, or near, the surface.

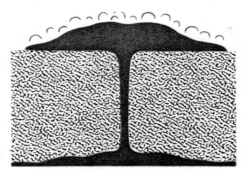

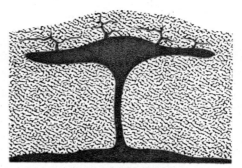

Molten rock forced up to the surface is called extrusive: it flows as lava from a volcano; cools to form solid sheets of rock.

Molten rock which is forced up, but does not reach the surface, is called intrusive. It cools as solid blobs and plugs underneath.

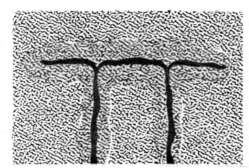

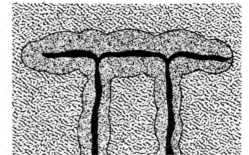

Molten intrusions may 'cook' and change surrounding rock; this is called metamorphic.

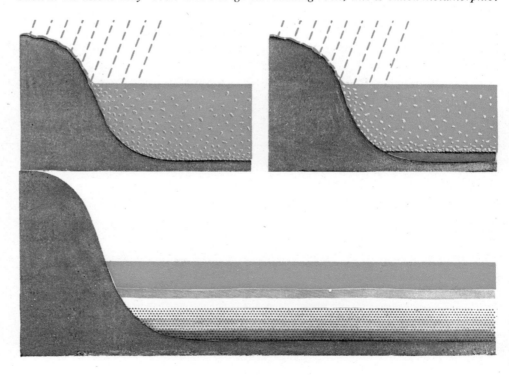

Once the seas were formed, erosion began. Rains washed the plant-less earth into the sea; layers of sediments formed on its bottom, became compressed into true rock. Often these beds became bent or folded by movements of the earth's crust, and raised into mountains, so that now we can find them, with their fossils, thousands of feet above sea level.

Ages and periods, in their relative lengths, are shown progressively in panels on this and succeeding pages. The panel opposite represents the time just before fossils.

FIRST AGE OF LIFE

What the first living things were like we can only guess: they were certainly single-celled. What we can call the First Age of Life, lasting for over 250 million years, began about 500 million years ago with living things that left fossils. The first period of this age was a time of molluscs, although there were other quite complicated animals like graptolites and some jointed, hard-shelled trilobites (both shown in panel). In the periods which followed, life, as shown below, still existed only in the sea. For a hundred million years life was dominated by seaweeds, jointed animals and molluscs. The big animal with tentacles is a nautiloid – a kind of mollusc. It is catching a blue trilobite. Another kind of trilobite swims above it and to the right. On the left is a sea-scorpion and another kind swims behind it. The objects with stalks and tentacles are animals known as crinoids. Many corals (which are also animals) grow on the sea floor.

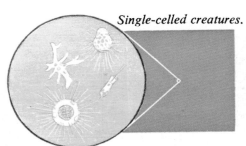
Single-celled creatures.

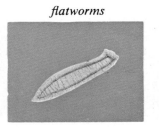
flatworms

algae (seaweeds)

sponges

These are early forms of life, including the single-celled creatures (magnified here) with properties of both animals and plants.

THE TIME OF MOLLUSCS

FIRST AGE
Mollusc

During the first period of the First Age there was little movement of the earth's crust. But the period which followed – a time of fish – was one of sudden and violent movement. When it began, about 300 million years ago, the earth underwent a succession of upheavals, forming great 'crinkles' in the crust. Layers of rock which had previously been under water, were lifted up and folded; often land areas sank, and the sea covered them.

The folding of the crust which forms mountains is sometimes very complicated; at other times it is simple, and the land resembles a wrinkled table-cloth. As the forces increase, the folds are squeezed together and may finally tumble over. Although to-day the surface of the land seems changed beyond all recognition, we can still see evidence of this time of mountain-building – in Scotland and Norway, Brazil and south of the St. Lawrence River in North America.

While these movements were going on, life colonized the land for the first time. The first invaders from the sea were plants; they were followed by some simple, jointed animals. In the sea, evolution continued with the rise of some fish-like creatures called ostracoderms and some true fish. Many of these early fish-animals were curiously armoured. Some of the nautiloids became coiled. At the right is a lung-fish, the first back-boned animal to go ashore. He is the ancestor of amphibians, reptiles, birds and mammals.

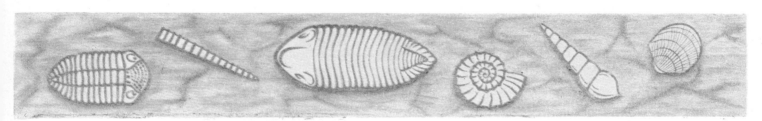

Some typical fossils of the First Age of Life; trilobites and molluscs, all animals which were divided into a number of segments.

THE TIME OF FISH

FIRST AGE
Fish

FIRST AGE
Mollusc

Towards the end of the First Age of Life came a great period of coal-forming – the Carboniferous, which lasted for over 50 million years. This was a period when life, while continuing to colonize the land, spread also into the air in the form of winged insects. It was a time, too, of a definite rhythm of upward and downward movement of the earth's crust. The great forests of early tree-like plants were often drowned and buried by sediments and in time their remains became coal. The chief coal-makers were very tall plants with spreading roots. Huge reeds and fern-like plants grew in the swamps near the mouths of rivers and made coal, too. Coal was also formed in several other periods, but mostly in the Carboniferous.

In the marshy forests of this period, seen below, we find early amphibians. The wide-headed creature is a stegocephalian and the crocodile-like animal a giant salamander. Note the flowerless trees and the big dragonfly, one of the earliest insects. There were no birds or reptiles.

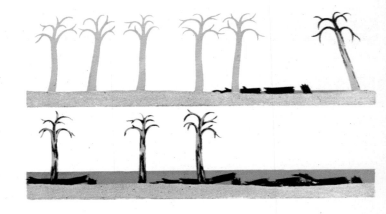

Trees die and decay on the ground. A downward movement of the earth's crust drowns the carboniferous forest. Under the sea, the dead tree-stuff is buried under sand and mud; forms a seam of coal.

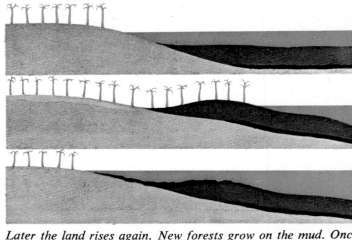

Later the land rises again. New forests grow on the mud. Once more land sinks; a second drowned forest forms new coal above the old. Thus several layers of coal often occur, one on the other.

FIRST AGE
Insect

FIRST AGE
Fish

FIRST AGE
Mollusc

SECOND AGE OF LIFE

The First Age of Life ended a little over 200 million years ago; with great changes in the earth's surface. The marshes dried up. New and more advanced kinds of plants established themselves on dry land, and some of the new forms of animal life were vastly different from those which were dying out. They inhabited the sea, the land and the air, and made a bridge, or link, between the ancient forms of the First Age of Life and those we see to-day. These new creatures evolved from the amphibians, but unlike the amphibians, did not need water for the growth of their young. They were the first reptiles. By the end of the First Age, there were many different sorts of reptiles; but during the Second Age of Life a special group of reptiles, the dinosaurs, came to dominate the earth's surface in a dramatic way. In the early period of the Second Age of Life there were great deposits of sediment. On land there were desert-like conditions and the seas were alternately shallow and deep. What rains there were, washed the crumbled rock into the sea, forming great layers of sand. At the same time the sea was full of single-celled animals with hard, but chalky shells. When they died, their shells fell to the bottom and formed thick layers. This became compressed to make chalk rock, which in places is very thick. Earth movements, long after, have raised the chalk above the sea. Besides the chalk, which came from sea-animals, huge deposits of

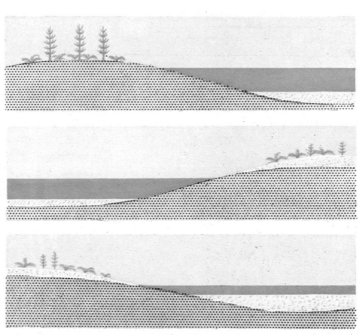

Alternate raising and sinking of land above and below sea level.

sediments were formed in the Second Age of Life as a result of erosion. Fine mud, washed down from the hills, settled far out in seas and lakes to form clay and sands. When animals of the Second Age died, they often did so on these sediments, or were washed into them. Quickly they were overlaid by more sediments; their bones were thus preserved as fossils. The sedimentary rocks of this age of Life are thousands of feet thick and rich in fossils. Thus we have learned quite a lot about the animals of this age and their evolution.

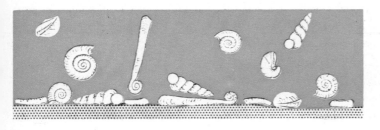

These are animals living in sea which is free from mud. As they die, their shells sink to the bottom and eventually become chalk.

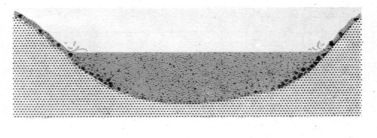

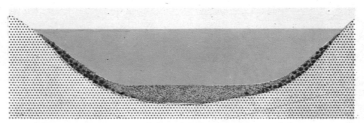

Particles of debris and animals collect in the water, gradually sinking to the bottom where they form a layer of material.

THE GREAT REPTILES

pterodactyl

SECOND AGE
Reptile

stegosaurus

brontosaurus

compsognathus

Some dinosaurs became the biggest animals ever to walk the earth's surface. Compare vast brontosaurus and stegosaurus with compsognathus, an ancestor of the mammals. Some dinosaurs flew on bat-like skin-wings stretched on their little fingers. Some returned to the sea and evolved there into whale-like creatures. In the picture below,

FIRST AGE
Insect

FIRST AGE
Fish

FIRST AGE
Mollusc

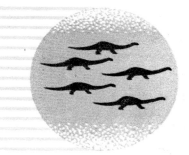
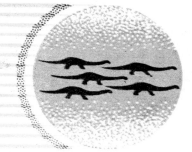

A rapid change of climate drove the dinosaurs into an ever-narrowing tropical belt.

the long tailed sea-creature is a mosasaur; that with a long neck, a plesiosaur. A trachodon crawls ashore; behind it is a herd of vast diplodocus. On the right, the terrible dinosaur-of-prey, tyrannosaurus, kills a stegosaurus by attacking its unprotected belly. In the middle distance is the ostrich-like struthiomimus; in the right distance, triceratops. On the tree is the earliest known feathered animal, the reptile-bird archaeopteryx. Lords of the air then were winged dinosaurs, the pterodactyls. The largest (shown here) was pteranodon.

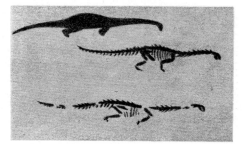

Fossil bones are all that is left of them.

THIRD AGE OF LIFE

THIRD AGE
Mammal

SECOND AGE
Reptile

FIRST AGE
Insect

FIRST AGE
Fish

FIRST AGE
Mollusc

During the 100 million years of the Second Age there evolved a group of warm-blooded animals, small at first, which were to inherit the earth when the great reptiles became extinct. For 75 million years, since the beginning of the Third Age, these animals, the mammals, have dominated the earth. They have reached, in the sea, the greatest size ever reached by animals. On land none was ever as big as the biggest dinosaur, but baluchitheres and mammoths weighed many tons.

The animals of the Third Age shown in the picture did not all live at the same time, or in the same kind of place. To the right of the grey baluchithere is a giant armadillo, glyptodon. The giant sloth, megatherium, is at the tree; by it is a sabre-tooth. In the distance are mammoths; in the sea a right whale; in the tree a tarsier, a monkey and male and female ape-man (these probably once lived in trees in families). Among the birds are some living species— oystercatcher, egret, curlew, flamingo, Canada goose, eagle, chaffinch, peacock; and some extinct ones – great auk, giant albatross, the twelve-foot moa, and the curious flightless bird, phororhacos. In the sea are marlin, herring, wolf-fish, shark, john-dory, sun-fish, corals, and sea-anemones.

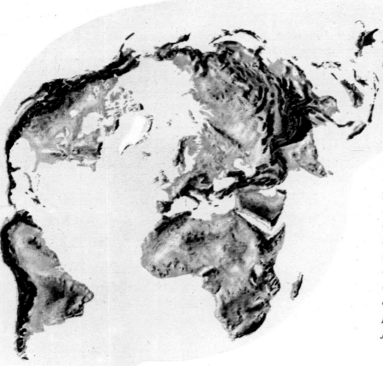

AN AGE OF MOUNTAIN-BUILDING.

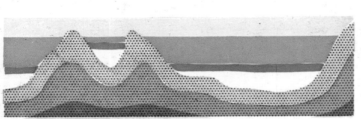

At first, sedimentary rocks lie horizontal, just as they were formed.

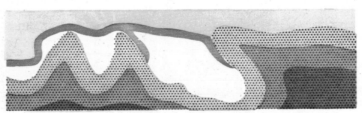

Next, movements of the earth's crust fold these layers of rock.

Erosion wears away these strata, exposing rocks of different ages.

baluchithere
mammoth
giant pig
modern boar

eohippus (first horse)

THIRD AGE
Mammal

SECOND AGE
Reptile

FIRST AGE
Insect

FIRST AGE
Fish

FIRST AGE
Mollusc

FOURTH AGE
Man

THIRD AGE
Mammal

SECOND AGE
Reptile

FIRST AGE
Insect

FIRST AGE
Fish

FIRST AGE
Mollusc

FOURTH AGE OF LIFE

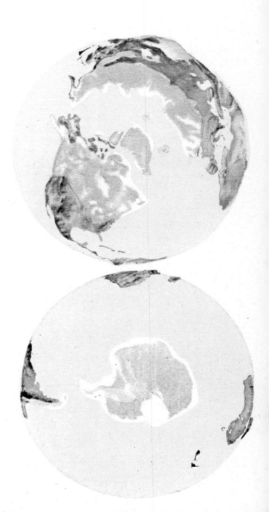

About a million years ago the Third Age of Life ended with a climate-change, known as the Ice Age (or Ages). The polar ice moved so far south that it more than once covered parts of Europe, Asia and North America that are now densely inhabited by humans. The maps show the furthest extreme of this ice. Four times the ice came down; four times it retreated; each time it left behind great deposits of muck and rubble which covered the ground and dammed back vast lakes of water. Needless to say, this million years was a great testing-time for animals, and only the most adaptable of them survived outside what are now the tropical belts, which were then still warm.

During the Ice Ages, man developed the use of tools, mainly made from flints, and thus a way of protecting himself against hazards; this led him to a new kind of life. At the end of the last Ice Age, fifteen thousand years ago, we find him an intelligent hunter and an artist as good as any since.

As the ice retreated, low plants gave way to trees; man and bears, both adaptable animals, were among the first to return.

His intelligence sharpened by a long battle with the climate, man, with his tools, became the greatest hunting animal.

He learned the use of berries and roots, how to make fire, how to cook, how to clothe himself, how to make a safe shelter.

16

FOURTH AGE
Man

THIRD AGE
Mammal

SECOND AGE
Reptile

FIRST AGE
Insect

FIRST AGE
Fish

FIRST AGE
Mollusc

MAN'S AGE OF LIFE

We call our own species of man *Homo sapiens*, which means knowing man; and certainly we are the most intelligent of animals. Many things distinguish man from those living animals most similar to him – his upright position; his higher brain capacity and complexity, which has enabled him to store knowledge and hand it down from generation to generation; his use of tools; his inability to defend himself except with weapons; his capacity for spiritual worship; and the ability to be more kind and more wicked to members of his own species than any other living creature.

The Fourth Age of Life, which belongs to man, is an age of a new kind of progress – human invention. Things that seem simple to us were once revolutionary discoveries; boats, rope, pottery, the wheel, the arch, the axe, the lever, the saw, the loom, were invented, some more than once, in different parts of the world.

What do we mean by civilization? How has man come to lead his present life, so complicated that he finds himself difficult to understand and even more difficult to manage? Man's advance was step by step; from a hunting life with fire, tools and the gathering of wild plants by families, to tribes and village groups who cultivated food in the summer to store for the winter; from little towns with trade and barter and the division of work to big towns with systems of government and special religions. Man did not reach the same state of learning all over the world at the same time. The greatest source of ideas, methods and inventions, from which we of the west trace our own, were the civilizations of Mesopotamia (Babylonia) and Egypt; then those of Greece and Rome. These gave us what is still the most powerful tool of man, the written record, with alphabet and numerals. The Greeks and Romans, who first invented the idea of government by popular consent, began what the Europeans usually call history.

We have now brought our story from the dawn of life to the time of history. But before we can see how man is using his inheritance today, we must look more closely at the earth itself. We must see how it works, what it is made of, what grows on it, what wonders and what challenges it presents.

Some men were already farmers about 8,000 years ago, with enclosed villages, domestic animals and clearings where they grew grain.

Over 4,000 years ago there were real towns in Mesopotamia. With metal, stone, wood, man became sailor, soldier, sculptor and builder.

Man stores knowledge by written symbols. At first he wrote with pictures; but for 3,000 years he has used alphabet and numerals.

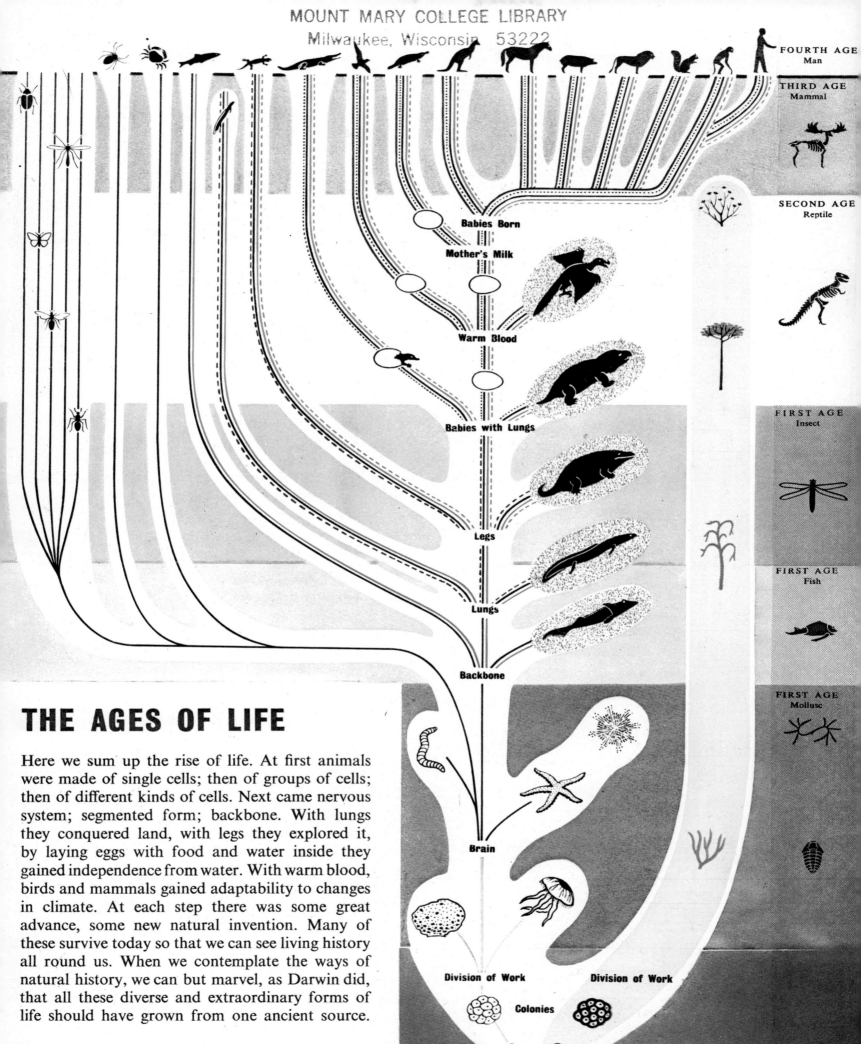

FOURTH AGE
Man

THIRD AGE
Mammal

SECOND AGE
Reptile

FIRST AGE
Insect

FIRST AGE
Fish

FIRST AGE
Mollusc

Babies Born

Mother's Milk

Warm Blood

Babies with Lungs

Legs

Lungs

Backbone

Brain

Division of Work

Division of Work

Colonies

Single Cell

LIFE BEGINS

THE AGES OF LIFE

Here we sum up the rise of life. At first animals were made of single cells; then of groups of cells; then of different kinds of cells. Next came nervous system; segmented form; backbone. With lungs they conquered land, with legs they explored it, by laying eggs with food and water inside they gained independence from water. With warm blood, birds and mammals gained adaptability to changes in climate. At each step there was some great advance, some new natural invention. Many of these survive today so that we can see living history all round us. When we contemplate the ways of natural history, we can but marvel, as Darwin did, that all these diverse and extraordinary forms of life should have grown from one ancient source.

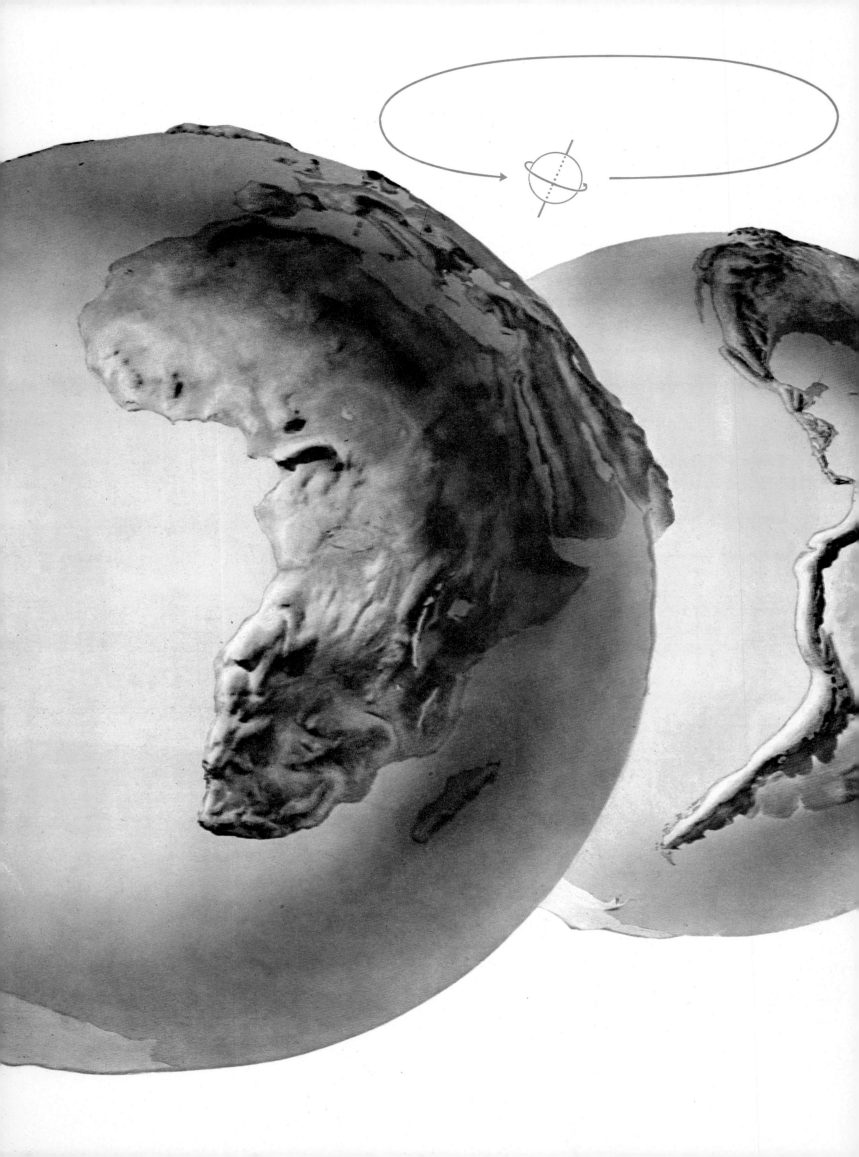

II
The Face of The World

THE EARTH: a ball on whose surface is fifty-five million square miles of land and one hundred and forty-one million square miles of water.

Time is never still on earth; nights follow days, summers follow winters, calms follow storms.

Eternally the earth's surface changes, shaped and re-shaped by forces outside and inside its crust; by the sun and moon, the earth's own spin and internal heat, by rain, snow, ice, by sea-current, tide and wind, by earthquake and eruption. The earth's great carpets of plants and the communities of animals that live on them are always changing too.

THE EARTH AROUND THE SUN

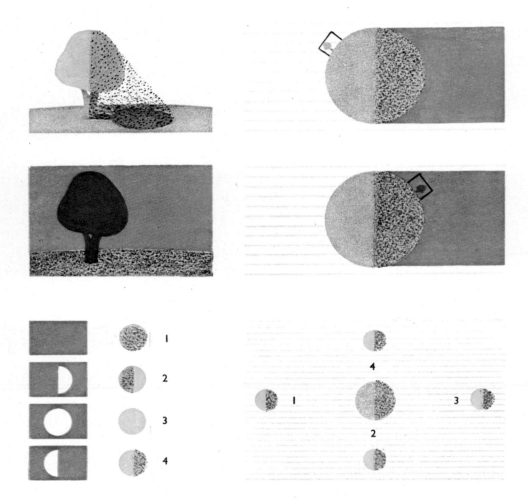

The earth rotates on its own axis once in every twenty-four hours. Any one place on the surface of the earth first faces the sun and then away from the sun; thus night follows day, and day follows night. As the earth rotates it also revolves round the sun, and one revolution takes about 365 days. The diagram shows one place on the earth's surface in the day and at night.

The Equator is an imaginary line round the middle of the earth. The surface between the Equator and the North Pole is the Northern Hemisphere; that between the Equator and the South Pole the Southern Hemisphere.

When the moon is 'new', it lies between earth and sun and the sun shines on the half turned away from the earth; when the moon is 'full' it lies on the side of the earth away from the sun and the sun shines on that half turned towards the earth. Between new moons there are two 'half' moons when the side of the moon facing the earth is half in light and half in dark. The moon takes $29\frac{1}{2}$ days to revolve once round the earth.

WE OWE THE SEASONS

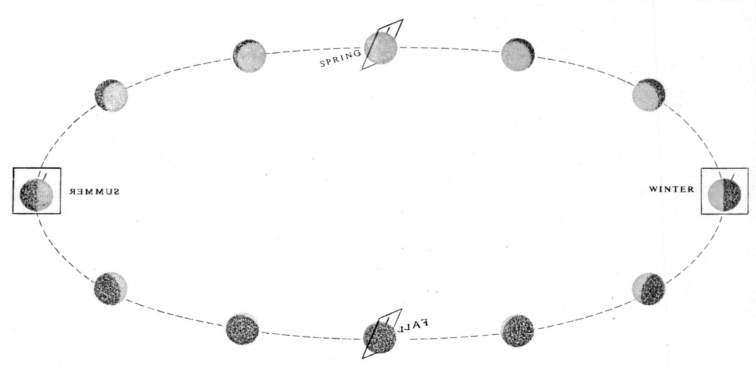

This shows positions of the earth as it revolves round the sun at each of the four seasons of the year in the northern hemisphere.

The angles at which the sun's rays fall on the earth determine its main temperature zones. Towards the Poles the sun is low, though it never sets in mid-summer. For the northern cool regions our symbol is the hardy cone-bearing tree. Nearer the equator, where the sun is higher, but never overhead, our symbol is the broad-leaved tree, and in the hotter dry regions of this temperate zone, the desert pine. For the tropics, which is the land lying between the Tropic of Cancer in the north and the Tropic of Capricorn in the south, where the sun is overhead at mid-day twice a year, our symbol is the palm tree.

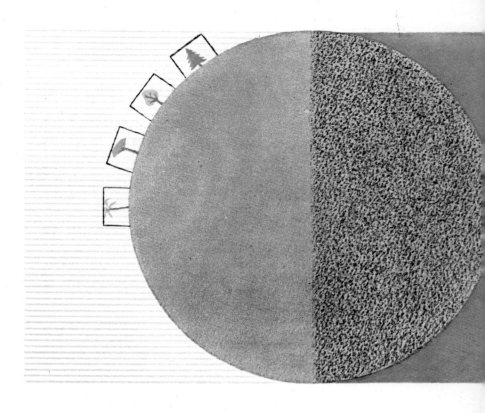

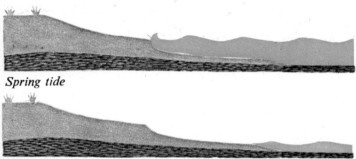

Spring tide

Neap tide

The pull of the moon and, to a lesser extent, sun on the sea makes tides. The difference between high and low tide is greatest when the moon and the sun pull together, shown above ('spring' tides), and least ('neap' tides) when their pulls are at right angles.

TO THE EARTH'S TILT

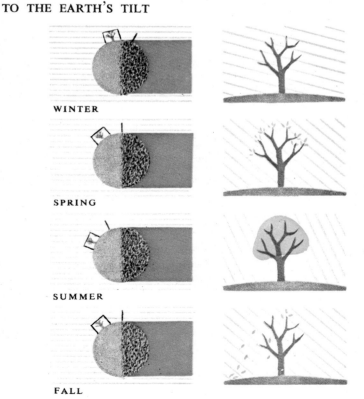

WINTER

SPRING

SUMMER

FALL

The earth's axis (between the Poles) is not at right angles to the plane of its orbit but tilted; so that north and south hemispheres each get more sun than the other for half the year.

At every point on the earth's surface, the angle at which the sun's 'rays' fall must consequently increase and decrease annually. Twice a year, at the spring and autumn equinoxes, night and day are of the same length; that is when the sun is overhead at the Equator. When the sun's rays are at their lowest in the northern hemisphere and it is midwinter there, they are at their highest in the southern hemisphere, where it is midsummer.

The Tropics of Cancer and Capricorn are imaginary lines, one to the north and the other to the south of the equator. They are the most northerly and southerly limits of the overhead sun. On the polar side of the Arctic and Antarctic Circles, the sun is above the horizon at midnight at least once a year; and below the horizon at noon once a year.

23

SUN SHINES, RAIN FALLS

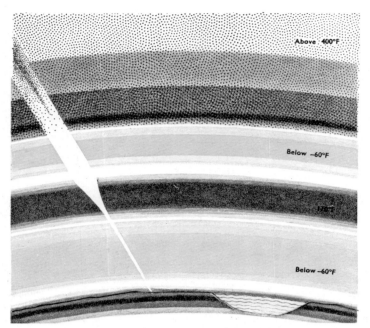

Above and below the narrow belt of life at the earth's surface, the temperature changes rapidly and reaches great extremes.

There are other planets in the universe, besides Earth, on which life probably exists. But life is almost certainly impossible without air, water and carbon, and at temperatures much higher or lower than those usual on the face of the earth.

On Earth there is no life on some always-frozen parts of the land, in some hot volcanic springs, and in some quite waterless deserts. But something living can be found almost everywhere else; from deepest ocean to highest mountain.

Once, in California in July, a thermometer showed 134 degrees (Fahrenheit) in the shade; and once, in Oymekon in eastern Siberia in February, another showed minus 90 degrees, or 122 degrees of frost. These are the most extreme air temperatures ever recorded on the earth's surface.

At night land loses heat rapidly and cools; as the sun rises the soil and surrounding air heat up; land cools again as sun sets.

WHERE THE WORLD IS HOT

On average the hottest place is the Red Sea (about 90 degrees) and the coldest probably the South Pole (below minus 20 degrees). Some algae (very simple plants) can live in hot springs at 175 degrees (hot drink temperature), and some very simple animals can stand 130 degrees. Several beetles and worms can live at 115. But higher animals have to have 'built-in' cooling arrangements to live at over 105 degrees. Man seems to succeed best where the temperature is usually between 30 and 45 in winter, and between 55 and 75 in summer. Most land with this range lies in the North Temperate Zone; the South Temperate Zone is mainly sea.

◯Under 32°F   32°–50°F   50°–60°F   60°–70°F   70°–80°F   Over 80°F

Fibre-like clouds, 20,000 feet up, are cirrus; top-left are altocumulus about 10,000 feet; the great mass is cumulonimbus as low as 2,000 feet.

Sun's heat evaporates water, forms cloud ; if cloud is blown to a cooler place, or to a mountain, rain falls ; if to a warmer place, it disappears.

WHERE THE WORLD IS WET

Life zones depend as much on water as on temperature. Some parts of the earth, of which the Sahara is by far the largest, get no rain for years at a time. Assam, in Asia, and Hawaii are probably the wettest places in the world, with an average rainfall (in spots) of over 400 inches. Forty inches have fallen in Assam in a day! The rainy places are mostly where warm winds from equatorial seas meet cool mountain ranges, and spill their water: the dry places, where cool winds meet warm land. Most of the tropics have summer rains; the densest tropical forests have rain all the year round. In the temperate regions the interiors of the great continents have rather little rain, and that mostly in spring; but nearer the coasts there is moderate rainfall throughout the year. Man seems to succeed best where not less than 20 and not more than 60 inches of rain are spread evenly over the year.

Under 10"　　10"–25"　　25"–50"　　50"–75"　　Over 75"

25

WINDS BLOW

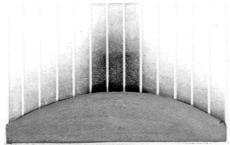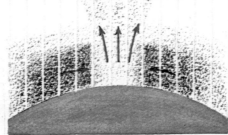

Heated by the sun, air expands, therefore becomes less dense. It rises, is replaced by cooler, heavier air. Air is thus circulated.

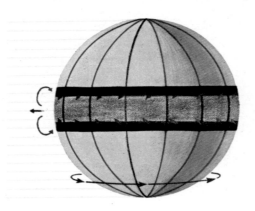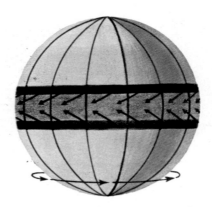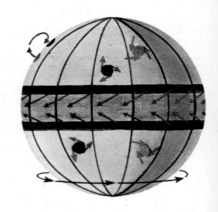

Air over the equator gets most heat from the sun. This causes a perpetual circulation as cool air moves towards the equator from both hemispheres. As the earth spins, all places travel from west to east, and fastest at the equator. The spin carries the air with it, of course; but there is some 'drag'—the air tends to get slightly 'left-behind'. Thus, equator-going cool winds become deflected from east to west, giving equatorial regions prevailing east winds. The return circulation gives the

temperate regions to the north and south prevailing west winds. In the diagram, high-pressure (dense) air is dark brown, the low-pressure (light) air is pale brown. Wind blows from a high-pressure area. It is deflected westwards on the equator side by the earth's rotation. In the northern hemisphere, winds flow clockwise round high-pressure areas ('highs'), and anti-clockwise round low-pressure areas ('lows'); in the southern hemisphere winds blow in the opposite way round 'highs' and 'lows'.

WHERE WINDS BLOW

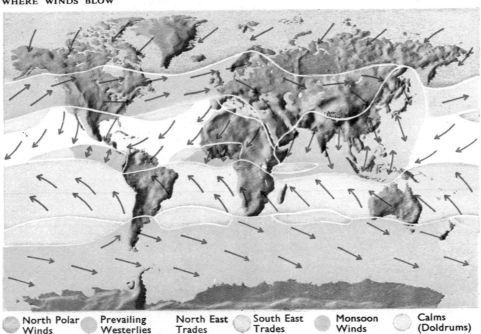

North Polar Winds	Prevailing Westerlies	North East Trades	South East Trades	Monsoon Winds	Calms (Doldrums)

Like the winds, the main sea-currents near the equator run from east to west, and in the temperate regions from west to east. All have a great influence on life. Thus although Britain is at the same latitude as Labrador, it has a much better climate (for man) because it is bathed by the warm current which starts as the Gulf Stream and flows northeast to become the North Atlantic or West Wind Drift. At the Tropics of Cancer and Capricorn, on the west sides of the Americas, Africa and Australia, cool currents bathe desert coasts, and the sea is richer in life than land. A cold current flows eastward round the Antarctic continent.

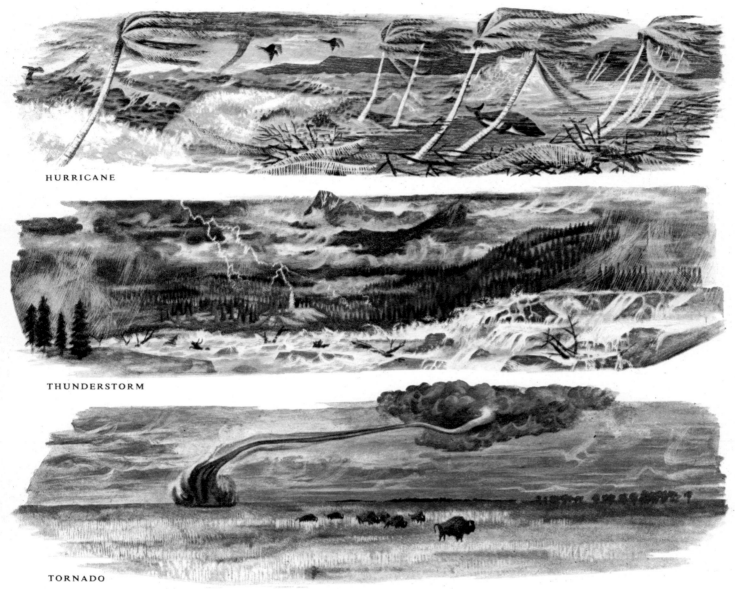

HURRICANE

THUNDERSTORM

TORNADO

Storms, with their hurricanes, floods and tidal waves, can destroy and disperse more animals and plants, and change nature more quickly and thoroughly, than all man's atom-bombs put together (so far!) and there is nothing man can do to prevent them.

SOME FAMOUS STORMS

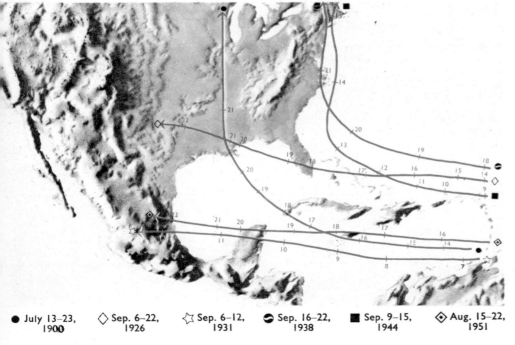

● July 13–23, 1900   ◇ Sep. 6–22, 1926   ☆ Sep. 6–12, 1931   ◓ Sep. 16–22, 1938   ■ Sep. 9–15, 1944   ◈ Aug. 15–22, 1951

Storms occur all over the world, but most of all on the east coasts of the continents near the Tropics of Cancer and Capricorn where they are occasional and violent.

The United States Weather Bureau tracks hurricanes so carefully that they are far from an inhabited shore when warnings are sent out. Because of their early warning the terrible Jamaica hurricane of August 1951 killed only ten people.

Europe is the most storm-free of the continents; so much so that when storms come, man is often taken unawares; thus in the tragic North Sea surge of 1953, people were caught totally unprepared. Over a thousand drowned in England and Holland.

PLANTS GROW

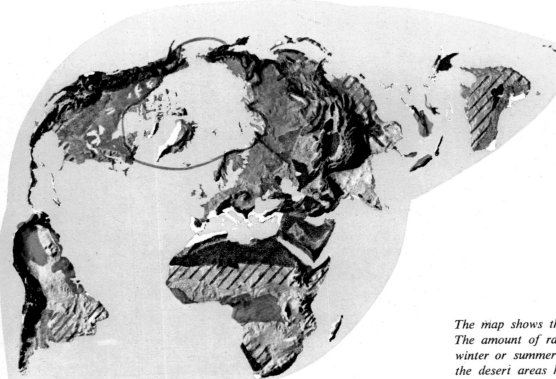

How could the different climatic regions of the Earth be shown without man, even though he does not really belong to this part of the book? There is no other creature found all over the world, far less one that wears different clothes in different climates.

The climate zones in which man is most successful, and can support the highest populations are maritime, Mediterranean and dry tropical. The greatest number and variety of wild plants, animals and insects is in the wet tropical zone. This is the only one in which man is not (yet) everywhere the dominant animal.

The map shows the twelve main climate zones of the world. The amount of rainfall and the main season when it occurs, winter or summer, varies from zone to zone. In some zones, the desert areas have very little rainfall or none at all. The temperature differs from region to region, and in some cases not only varies from winter to summer, but from night to day.

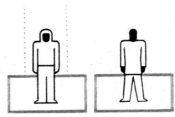

SUB-POLAR
very cold winter, cool summer

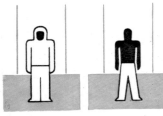

COLD CONTINENTAL
very cold winter, warm summer

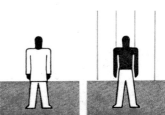

PRAIRIE
cool winter, warm summer

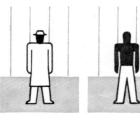

MARITIME
cool winter, warm summer

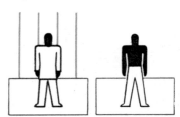

MEDITERRANEAN
mild winter, hot summer

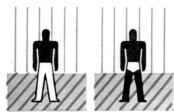

HUMID TEMPERATE
warm winter, very hot summer

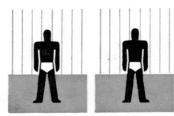

WET TROPICAL
very hot all the year

DRY TROPICAL
very hot all the year

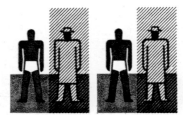

DESERT
cool night, very hot day

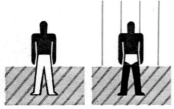

SEMI-DESERT (HOT)
warm winter, very hot summer

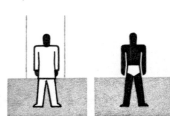

SEMI-DESERT (COOL)
cool winter, very hot summer

MOUNTAIN
very cold night, mild day

The land's surface is divided between three main kinds of vegetation – forest, grassland and desert. These three occur in both hot and cool regions.

TROPICAL FOREST

TROPICAL GRASSLAND

CONIFEROUS FOREST (CONE-BEARING TREES)

MOUNTAIN (ALPINE PLANTS)

DESERT

TEMPERATE GRASSLAND

SEMI-DESERT

DECIDUOUS FOREST (BROAD-LEAVED TREES)

Forests can grow where the ground is not permanently frozen, there is plenty of water and little wind. When rain is short, or markedly seasonal, grassland dominates; when water is scanty or lacking, the land becomes desert. In a journey from a desert plain up into wet mountains, the desert will soon give way to grass, and this to broad-leaved trees. Above these will be cone-bearing trees, which do not lose so much water by wind-evaporation. Farther up the wind is so strong that their place is taken by shrubs, low alpine plants, mosses and lichens. Vegetation belts on such a journey uphill closely resemble the much longer journey 'on the flat' from, say, the Sahara to the Arctic tundra.

WORK OF WIND AND WATER

Gradually, inevitably, rain and rivers wash and carry earth down from the hills. Full of silt, the rivers slow down in the valley and drop this silt as alluvium on the plain.

They meander through their own alluvium. Soft mud-banks on the outside of loops easily wash away; mud is deposited on the inside, loops become exaggerated and many are finally cut off as ox-bows. When they reach the sea, rivers still drop mud and form deltas with many mouths. Sometimes these deltas extend into the sea, like a bulge or as fingers of gravel and sand gradually growing further seaward.

A river flows down the slope; gradually it carries earth downhill.

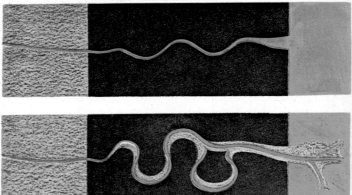

A young river flows quickly; an old river meanders, drops its load.

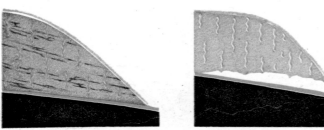

Water trickles through some rocks, dissolves others; when it reaches hard rock it flows down the dip to emerge as springs.

Waterfalls can form where soft rock is sandwiched between hard. Slowly water cuts back the soft rock, forming a vertical step.

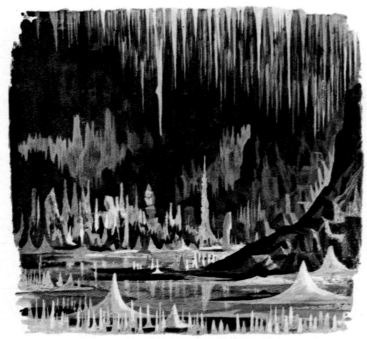

A LIMESTONE CAVE

NIAGARA FALLS

The Grand Canyon of the Colorado River, in Arizona, the largest and finest example of the work of running water in the world.

Frost, rain, wind work at a cliff, erode it most quickly at top, and clothe it at bottom in an apron of its own pieces, called talus.

A running river cuts down through many strata. Rain and frost erode the walls. Hard beds form cliffs; soft beds form shelves.

TALUS SLOPES IN THE EASTERN ALPS

The Grand Canyon was cut by the Colorado River and its tributaries through a slowly-rising dome of stratified rock. It is 217 miles long, from 4 to 18 miles wide and a mile deep. The river at its bottom carries away nearly half a million tons of silt a day! The Canyon is in a dry region with sparse vegetation, liable to sudden rain-storms which erode very powerfully. If Arizona were moist, plants would densely cover the slopes, and the erosion would go much more slowly.

There are three main types of erosion – water, frost and wind. In water erosion, rock is carried down-river as particles in suspension, sand and mud; or in solution, dissolved limestone. When frost occurs, water in cracks freezes and expands, forcing the rocks to break up. Wind, in dry countries especially, scours rocks away with sand and dust.

WORK OF SEA AND ICE

Destructive waves attack, and gradually erode the cliff faces.

Gentle waves deposit sand and pebbles, building up the beach.

ST. KILDA, SCOTLAND

VIRGINIA COAST, U.S.A.

Constantly the sea attacks the land, breaks rock and grinds it into pebbles, gravel and grains of sand. This sand may sink to form a shallow shelf round the land, and some of it may be driven by currents, tides and waves to be added to a nearby beach.

Cliff erosion and beach-building can be seen almost everywhere on the coasts of Britain and the Western United States. The Gulf and Atlantic coasts of the U.S. form practically one long beach from Texas, round the tip of Florida, to northern New England.

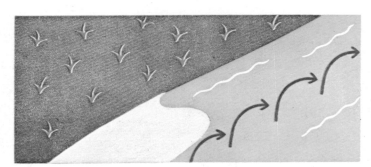

Beach material is often driven along a coast by waves and tides to form a bar with a lagoon inside. Chesil Beach in Dorset, England, is an unbroken

ridge of pebbles, 18 miles long. This ridge would have continued growing into the English Channel had it not come up against rocky Portland Island.

CHESIL BEACH, DORSET

A Glacier in the Rockies: note the moraine where it ends, the lower smoothed slopes in this scene show the old work of ice.

The world of many of us looks the way it does because of the work of ice. During the Ice Age, not many thousands of years ago, ice-sheets and glaciers covered about half North America and Europe – two-thirds of the British Isles. The vast areas from which the ice has now retreated are covered with 'drift' material transported by the glaciers, and dumped, miles from where it came, when the ice finally melted.

Glaciers are true rivers of ice, for they really flow. The ice-caps they start from are formed by the compression of snow under its own weight. As they scrape their way down-valley the ice-rivers gather rocks at their sides, and carry side moraines; when two glaciers join, a central moraine is formed. These moraines are piles of debris which have been gathered by the glacier on its journey. Big ice-caps only survive in the world at great heights, as in the Himalayas; or in the Polar Regions. The Antarctic Continent and Greenland are covered with ice-sheets thousands of feet thick, through which mountain-tops poke here and there. Scientists think that if Greenland's ice melted, a group of islands might be found underneath.

At present most ice-caps and glaciers in the world are melting in summer a bit faster than they form in winter. An edge of one ice-cap in Iceland has shrunk about a mile in the last fifty years.

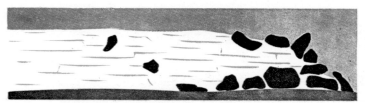

The glacier advances, carrying rocks it has scoured from the mountains. When it retreats it leaves behind an end moraine.

 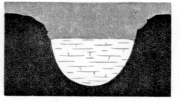

Glaciers scour valleys, make them smooth-sided and U-shaped.

MORE OF NATURE'S WORK

The formation of coral islands, or atolls, is a long and complicated process.

Many little floating sea-animals have shells, and when they die these shells fall to the bottom, and settle there as sediment, or 'ooze'. This gradually increases the height of the submarine banks. Sometimes earth-movements also raise the sea-bed. When the banks are near enough to the surface to get light, coral can grow on them, in the warmer seas. Coral animals are related to jelly-fish, but they have a hard skeleton outside them, which they leave behind when they die: upon dead skeletons new corals fix themselves. A coral colony then, grows outwards; for the new, living corals can only live in the shallows to a depth of a little over a hundred feet, at the edge of the mass of old coral. But the water needs to be free of sand, and not too salty, or else the coral animals suffocate. If the bank sinks the coral growth can keep pace with the sinking and the growing part is left as a ring-like reef; there is a lagoon inside. If the bank rises, parts of the reef are exposed and soil slowly forms on the dead coral. Eventually palms and other plants can grow on the island. Coral islands are found mostly in the tropical seas: they are particularly numerous in the Pacific, and there is a huge coral formation off the east coast of Australia – the Great Barrier Reef which stretches for over 1,300 miles. In the Keys of south Florida, the only part of the United States that is almost tropical, there are many miles of coral reef. It is interesting to think that new land is being constantly made by animals in the warm sections of the oceans.

The surface of the earth in many regions is still in a state of tension, and moves. Volcanoes erupt, and earthquakes shake the ground, with results far greater than hydrogen bombs. These wonders of nature are commonest along particular strips of the earth's crust, such as the Pacific coasts of Japan, the East Indies, Alaska and Central America, and Italy and Iceland; sometimes whole islands or towns are wrecked and much life destroyed.

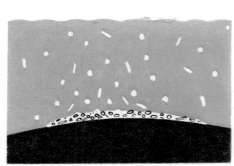 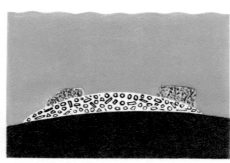 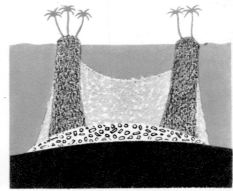

Falling sediments raise a bank under the sea to the light, so that coral can form an atoll, with its lagoon and ring of reef.

A TYPICAL ATOLL

Earthquakes change the landscape by producing faults and rifts.

A fault.

A rift, or double-fault.

THE THINGVELLIR RIFT, ICELAND

Under tension, cracks appear against the grain of the rock strata, one face of the crack slides up or down, often leaving a vertical cliff. The Thingvellir rift opened at the side of a valley whose floor caved in.

Some eruptions scatter ash-grains and debris: each eruption's ash becomes a layer.

Other eruptions spout mainly molten rock as lava-flows. These form layers of basalt.

VOLCANO SPOUTING BOTH ASH AND LAVA

Volcanoes erupt periodically – some even so regularly as to be almost predictable. In many volcanic regions the activity heats underground water and makes geysers and hot springs. Some spout continually.

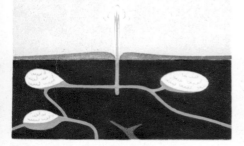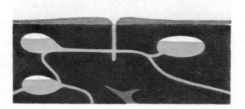

Volcanic energy sometimes heats water in pockets: steam rises, making a geyser.

A GEYSER, YELLOWSTONE PARK, U.S.A.

NATURE'S WORLD

III
Man's World

Man has inherited the earth. With engines he has changed the landscape so quickly that he cannot make new maps fast enough. Many a scene which once showed only forest, grass and wild animals has been changed by man in a few score years. He has cut, dammed, bulldozed, tunnelled and built across the face of the earth.

However, Nature is strong. Much wild country still defies all man's efforts to change it. On the other hand, man has found that misuse can destroy forests, wear out soil. He has had to learn that nature's resources are not inexhaustible and must be conserved to insure his own welfare and happiness.

MAN MUST EAT

Master of the world for about twenty thousand years, man spent the first two-thirds of this as a hunter. Only since about 5000 B.C. did he become a farmer, at first in fertile Mesopotamia and Egypt, learning to cultivate wild plants, crop and store them, improve and change them. As man spread he took his old plants with him and found new ones to domesticate, so the present distribution of cultivated plants is often quite different from that of the wild ones from which they are descended.

wheat and barley

barley only

maize and millet

oats and rye

rice

tea

coff

coc

Barley, wheat, millet came from Europe and the Mediterranean; rye, oats, rice, tea: Asia; coffee: Arabia; maize, cocoa: America.

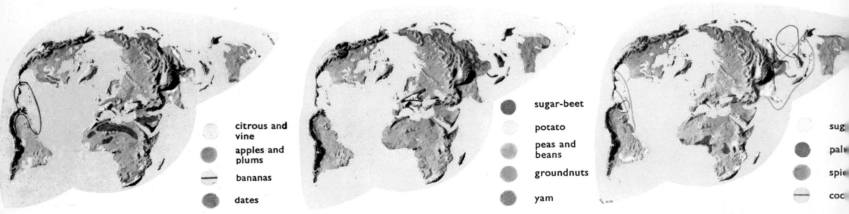

citrus and vine

apples and plums

bananas

dates

sugar-beet

potato

peas and beans

groundnuts

yam

sug

pal

spi

coc

Mediterranean vine, Chinese and Indian citrous fruits, American potato, East Indian spices: Food-plants' origins lie the world over.

In line, a group of combine mechanical harvesters reap their way across the vast fields of one of the world's great wheat-belts.

Round an Italian village crops of many kinds are still tended by hand; families work their own strips and small holdings.

38

	timber
	rubber
	cotton
	silk
	flax
	tobacco

TOBACCO

COTTON

RUBBER

JUTE

TEA

Not all plants are cultivated for food. Originally tobacco came from America, rubber from Brazil, tea from Asia, cotton from China, flax from the Mediterranean, jute from India. Silk, spun by a moth-caterpillar that lives only on mulberry-leaves, came from China.

MAN AND ANIMALS

Domestic Animals

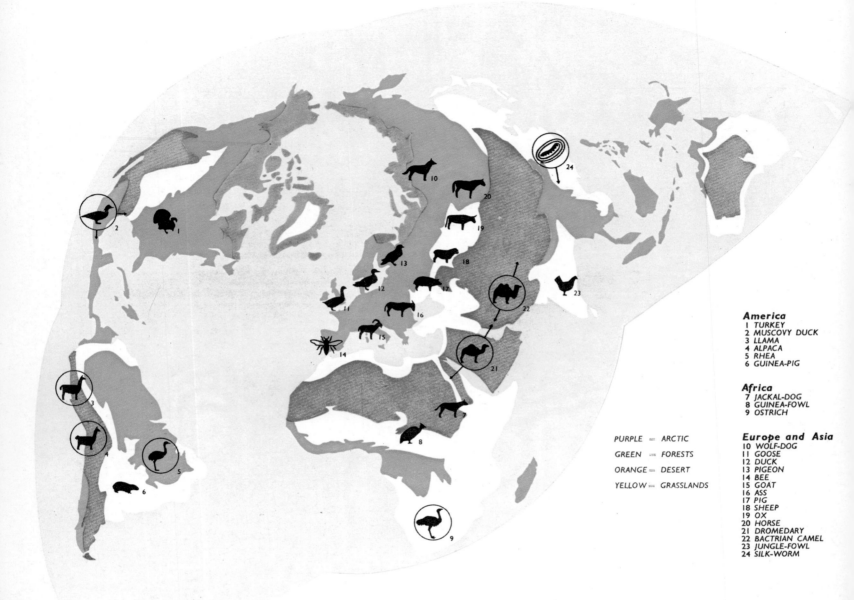

America
1 TURKEY
2 MUSCOVY DUCK
3 LLAMA
4 ALPACA
5 RHEA
6 GUINEA-PIG

Africa
7 JACKAL-DOG
8 GUINEA-FOWL
9 OSTRICH

PURPLE = ARCTIC
GREEN = FORESTS
ORANGE = DESERT
YELLOW = GRASSLANDS

Europe and Asia
10 WOLF-DOG
11 GOOSE
12 DUCK
13 PIGEON
14 BEE
15 GOAT
16 ASS
17 PIG
18 SHEEP
19 OX
20 HORSE
21 DROMEDARY
22 BACTRIAN CAMEL
23 JUNGLE-FOWL
24 SILK-WORM

Of some of the animals man has enslaved, those in circles have a rather restricted distribution.

Dogs are probably descended from both wolves and jackals. Their ancestors must have followed human hunters for the remains of the kill; occasionally their puppies must have been kept as pets, the first domestic animals, and grew to accept humans as foster parents.

When wolves hunt they work together and share the food; and dogs have kept this instinct to co-operate. They take quite naturally to hunting or retrieving man's game for him, accepting the share of food he gives them, and sharing and protecting their master's home.

Wild Animals

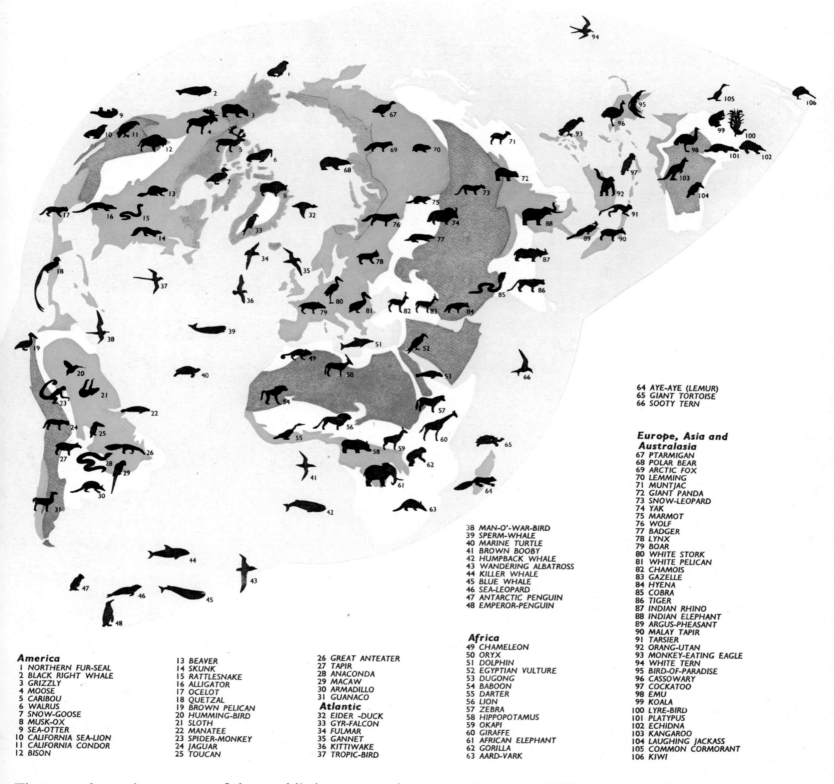

America
1 NORTHERN FUR-SEAL
2 BLACK RIGHT WHALE
3 GRIZZLY
4 MOOSE
5 CARIBOU
6 WALRUS
7 SNOW-GOOSE
8 MUSK-OX
9 SEA-OTTER
10 CALIFORNIA SEA-LION
11 CALIFORNIA CONDOR
12 BISON
13 BEAVER
14 SKUNK
15 RATTLESNAKE
16 ALLIGATOR
17 OCELOT
18 QUETZAL
19 BROWN PELICAN
20 HUMMING-BIRD
21 SLOTH
22 MANATEE
23 SPIDER-MONKEY
24 JAGUAR
25 TOUCAN
26 GREAT ANTEATER
27 TAPIR
28 ANACONDA
29 MACAW
30 ARMADILLO
31 GUANACO

Atlantic
32 EIDER -DUCK
33 GYR-FALCON
34 FULMAR
35 GANNET
36 KITTIWAKE
37 TROPIC-BIRD
38 MAN-O'-WAR-BIRD
39 SPERM-WHALE
40 MARINE TURTLE
41 BROWN BOOBY
42 HUMPBACK WHALE
43 WANDERING ALBATROSS
44 KILLER WHALE
45 BLUE WHALE
46 SEA-LEOPARD
47 ANTARCTIC PENGUIN
48 EMPEROR-PENGUIN

Africa
49 CHAMELEON
50 ORYX
51 DOLPHIN
52 EGYPTIAN VULTURE
53 DUGONG
54 BABOON
55 DARTER
56 LION
57 ZEBRA
58 HIPPOPOTAMUS
59 OKAPI
60 GIRAFFE
61 AFRICAN ELEPHANT
62 GORILLA
63 AARD-VARK
64 AYE-AYE (LEMUR)
65 GIANT TORTOISE
66 SOOTY TERN

Europe, Asia and Australasia
67 PTARMIGAN
68 POLAR BEAR
69 ARCTIC FOX
70 LEMMING
71 MUNTJAC
72 GIANT PANDA
73 SNOW-LEOPARD
74 YAK
75 MARMOT
76 WOLF
77 BADGER
78 LYNX
79 BOAR
80 WHITE STORK
81 WHITE PELICAN
82 CHAMOIS
83 GAZELLE
84 HYENA
85 COBRA
86 TIGER
87 INDIAN RHINO
88 INDIAN ELEPHANT
89 ARGUS-PHEASANT
90 MALAY TAPIR
91 TARSIER
92 ORANG-UTAN
93 MONKEY-EATING EAGLE
94 WHITE TERN
95 BIRD-OF-PARADISE
96 CASSOWARY
97 COCKATOO
98 EMU
99 KOALA
100 LYRE-BIRD
101 PLATYPUS
102 ECHIDNA
103 KANGAROO
104 LAUGHING JACKASS
105 COMMON CORMORANT
106 KIWI

The map above shows some of the world's interesting wild mammals, birds and reptiles. These are but a tiny sample of all the animals, of which there are over a million species. Three quarters of these are insects, only about 3,500 mammals, 8,600 birds, 5,500 reptiles and amphibians and 18,000 fishes. Only a few have become useful slaves to man; usually they have changed a good bit in doing so.

MAN AND MINERALS

Minerals are the chemical substances of which the earth is composed; and some of them are useful to man for making things, or for fuel. Few metals are found free; usually they are combined with other elements as salts. An ore is earth or rock containing salts from which a useful metal can be extracted commercially. The precious metal gold is found free in gravels, and in the old days nuggets were 'washed' in pans, shaking to the bottom because of their great weight. Many ores near the surface (like iron ore in Northamptonshire, England) can be mined by mechanical shovels in the open.

In 'panning', heavy gold sinks as lighter gravel is washed out.

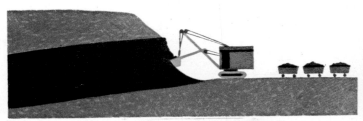

At an open-cast mine, ore is cut out and loaded at the surface.

Oil and coal, two of the earth's most valuable minerals, are man's chief source of fuel. Scientists believe oil was formed from the fat in bodies of little animals and plants that fell to the sea-bottom. Later sediments that formed on top of this 'ooze' became hard and heavy rock, which squeezed oil and salt water out of the ooze layer. This oil and water got trapped, where the rock above was folded. Sometimes gas was trapped, too, so that when a well is bored, the oil is forced up making a 'gusher'. But most often the oil has to be pumped up. Coal is composed mostly of the element carbon, and was formed from the compressed remains of plants. Most was laid down in the Carboniferous Period, between two and three hundred million years ago, in the First Age of Life, but some was formed even earlier, and some as late as the Third Age of Life. It is sometimes found in thick seams, but usually in seams no more, and often less than a man's height. Some coal is mined at the surface, but many seams are far underground, and mined in galleries from a central shaft. Even with modern tools, coalmining is hard and sometimes dangerous work. Britain has scarcely any natural oil, and coal is its most important resource of power. The United States is rich in both.

A well is bored down to the oil and the oil pumped to the surface.

A shaft is sunk, the coal dug from the seams which are richest.

gold, silver and diamonds

iron-ore

non-ferrous ores

coal and oil

Maps of minerals quickly change, from the Equator almost to the Poles as man seeks fuels like coal, oil, uranium; precious stones, like diamonds; metals, like gold, silver, platinum, and the commoner copper, lead, iron . . . Aluminium, the most abundant metal, is very hard to extract from its common ores; a rare ore, cryolite, makes this possible; it is mined at Ivigtut in Greenland, pictured here.

MAN AND POWER

Wind: the master of the waves and trees becomes the servant of the sailor and miller.

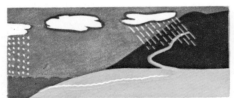

Water: rain on the mountain fills the river, turns a water-wheel, serves the miller.

Most power comes from the sun and its system. Winds and rain are caused by the sun's heat and the earth's spin; tides by the pull of the moon and the sun; volcanic heat probably radio-activity under the surface of the earth. The sun's heat comes from the changing of matter into energy by atomic fission; part of it received by the earth is about 1,000,000,000,000,000 horse-power. Plants use some of this to turn carbon dioxide and water into their own living substance; as they grow they store this energy up. So the energy of animals comes from the sun through the plants they eat.

Tide: high tide fills a basin, then makes electricity as it flows out through a turbine.

Animals: the word 'horse-power' shows that not long ago our only 'engines' were alive.

Earth's crust: besides coal and oil man can use steam and heat from volcanic sources, and atomic energy from radioactive minerals.

Opposite are many of the ways in which man collects, stores and uses energy. He stores water in valleys behind dams, to release it over turbines when he wants electric power. He makes electricity also with windmills, and by burning coal and oil in power-house engines. He stores electricity in batteries. He burns coal in steamers and railway-engines, and makes gas from it, which he stores in cylinders and distributes in pipes. He always uses oil in the light engines of aircraft and automobiles. Oil, a liquid, can be easily moved and stored; a refinery fills the bottom of the picture opposite.

MAN MUST TRAVEL

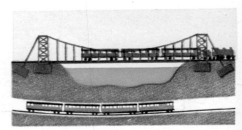

Crossing rivers: from rope-bridge to stone arch, from stage-coach to railroad, with its suspension-bridge above or under-river tunnel.

Crossing seas: from raft, which could only sail down-wind; to galleon, which had a keel and could tack; to steam-powered liner.

Crossing deserts: from camels, sure but slow, and unable to carry much; to fast motor-trucks; and now aircraft for through traffic.

Crossing mountains: roads wind and wriggle up to, and over the passes; railroads tunnel through; pressurized aircraft fly over.

Since he found the wheel and the horse, man has been the world's most capable traveller. He easily crosses mountains, ice-caps, deserts, forests and seas. Specialized animals can cross some of these, but only man can cross all. After more than a hundred years of machines, man has learned to ride on water at 200, on land at 400, and in rocket planes at over 1,600 miles an hour. But he is not as efficient as he would like to think. The principal roads of Britain, first laid by the Romans nearly two thousand years ago, were better fitted then for the traffic they had to carry than now. Seven hundred years ago the messengers of the Emperor of China, changing horses every three miles, could travel 400 miles in a day. Clipper-ships could sail 250 miles in a day, a distance few cargo-steamers exceed. There has been no great improvement in the speed of railroad-trains and steamships, or in the design of the bicycle, in the present century. Nobody has been able to improve the rowing-boat in hundreds of years.

Man finds it hard to manage his fast machines. His roads are too small, and cause accidents and jams. He can fly in less time from Boston to New York than it may take him to get from the airport to his office. Opposite is a city of the future that is quiet, clean and easy to get about in. But it will not be easy to pull down the old cities and build new ones.

46

LIFE IN PLAINS

The greatest concentrations of humans are nearly all in, or at the edges of, plains. It is quite easy to move, and carry goods about on a plain; and the soil is often fertile. Storms can sometimes be damaging, but the chief problem in plains life is the control of the distribution of water. Many coastal plains, such as those of Holland and East Anglia, have to be protected from sea-floods by walls. Some plains are marshy and waterlogged, and have to be carefully drained, sometimes with pumps; while others have too little water, and, to grow food, must be irrigated from rivers or canals. Most of the great plains of the world lie towards the interior of the Continents and are covered with grassland; the largest are in central Russia and North America.

SOUTH AMERICA: THE PAMPAS

NORTH AMERICA: THE PRAIRIE

HUNGARY: THE PUSZTA

EAST ANGLIA: THE FENS

Much land behind sea-walls has been won from the sea. More than half Holland is less than three feet above the level of the sea; huge areas are below it.

By drainage the Fens of East Anglia were changed, with a Dutch engineer's help, from peaty, salty bogs into some of the most fertile farmland in England.

The use of the grassland plains depends largely on the rainfall. In inland Queensland and New South Wales (above) water is scarce; sheep-farming, Australia's chief trade, is possible, but not much corn-growing. The sheep move from one grazing-ground to another. But over great stretches of the Steppes of Russia spring and summer rains make it possible to grow cereals instead of the natural grass. Members of a collective farm (above) get ready to thresh and gather in a crop of wheat.

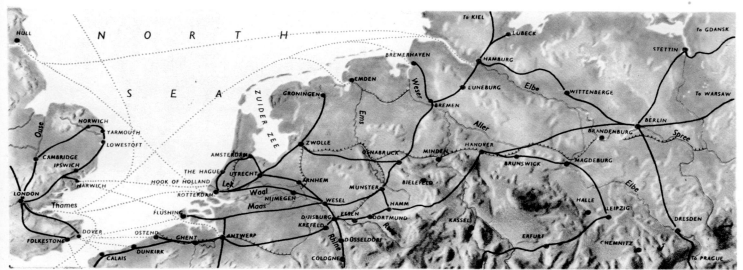

The plain of North-West Europe is fertile along its southern margin, but less so farther north. Berlin is the hub of communications.

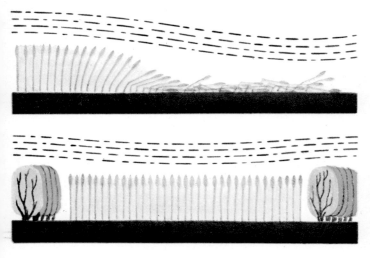
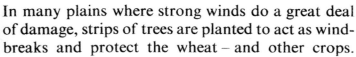

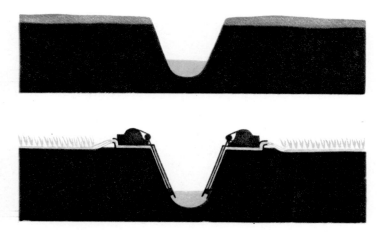

In many plains where strong winds do a great deal of damage, strips of trees are planted to act as wind-breaks and protect the wheat – and other crops.

In many dry regions such as those of Mesopotamia and Mexico, water can be lifted by pumps and spread over the country, to irrigate the crops.

LIFE IN MOUNTAINS

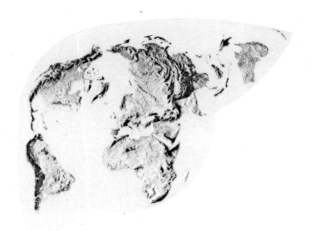

Because mountains are barriers the humans on each side of them often belong to different nations, and have different languages and customs; and many of the wild animals and plants are different, too. Mountain ranges usually have high snowfall or rainfall. The lower slopes of the valleys are often fertile, especially on the sides facing the Equator, which get most sun.

The principal mountain chains were all made by great movements of the earth's crust in the Third Age of Life, in Europe nearly all Iceland, the Pyrenees and Alps; in Asia the Himalayas and Caucasus; in Africa the Atlas; and in the America the great western walls—the Rockies and the Andes.

Snow falls in winter, and its spring melting brings down avalanches, from which mountain villages can be protected by a belt of trees.

  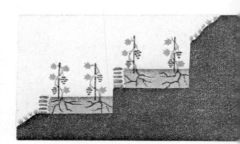

On the sunny side of the valley terraces are levelled for cultivation, gardens and roads.   Often houses have their front doors upstairs.

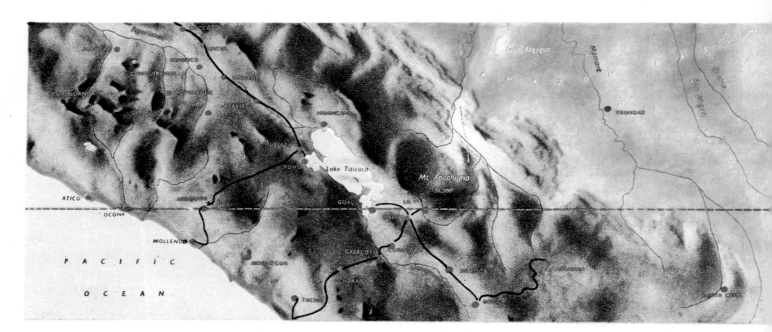

Innsbruck in the Alps, capital of the Austrian Tyrol.

Mount Kenya in East Africa.

The Rocky Mountains in Canada, with glacier, lake and forest.

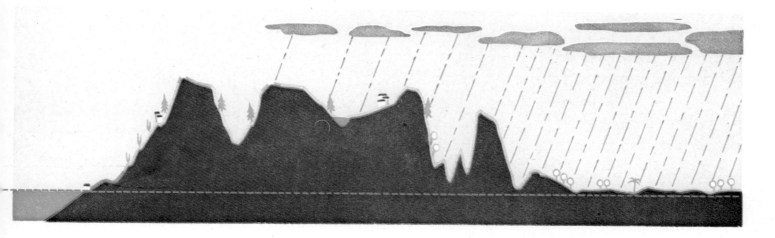

The map shows the Andes round Lake Titicaca, between Peru and Bolivia. Above is a section. Moist winds from the east sweep across the tropical forests of the Amazon, and drop their moisture on the eastern side of the Andes. On the west side, in Peru, hardly any rain falls: there is a desert strip.

51

LIFE BY RIVERS

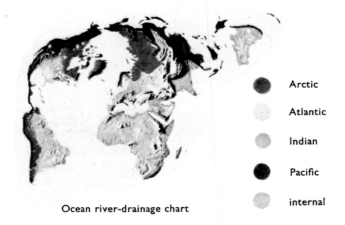

Ocean river-drainage chart

Arctic

Atlantic

Indian

Pacific

internal

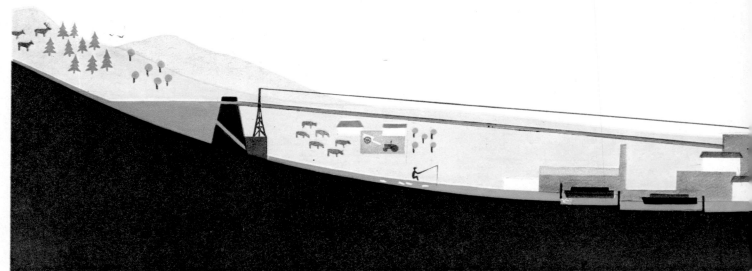

This diagram shows a section of a river from source to mouth, and all the uses which man has made of such a natural feature.

NORTH AMERICA'S WIDE MISSISSIPPI

JUNKS ON THE YANG-TZE-KIANG

The bottom lock-gate opens for the barge.

Both gates shut, and water fills the lock.

The top gate opens; the barge goes up.

Nearly every big river in the world is a life-line of Man. It was up the rivers that man first started nearly all his adventures of conquest and exploration. To-day he has shaped most of them to his purposes, the chief of which is trade. At the river-mouths he builds ports and shipyards, and his dredgers work to keep the ship-channels free. Farther up the rivers are towns and factories, with wharves: the things the towns buy and sell can be quickly and cheaply moved by boat. Nowadays man tries to keep his rivers free of town and factory waste, so that he may bathe and fish in them, while at the same time boats and barges can get far up by means of locks, and bring trade to the farmers there. In the steep hills from which the river rises man builds dams to supply his cities with power and water. He filters this water when he has used it, and returns it to the river. He has to look after his rivers, control and maintain them as carefully as if they were important roads—which, in a sense, they are.

The flatter regions, round the mouth of a river, usually attract man first, then gradually he spreads upstream towards the hills.

NILE, GREAT RIVER OF EGYPT

AMAZON, THE JUNGLE RIVER

INDIA'S SACRED RIVER GANGES

OXFORD CREWS ON THE THAMES

LIFE IN FORESTS

The forest is the climax of plant life. Before man came, most of Britain was covered with it; now less than one twentieth. Man has cleared many forests, though they still clothe much of the world. The hot, wet, tropical forests are dominated by deciduous (leaf-shedding) trees of many different sorts, like mahogany and teak. The world's biggest trees are the coniferous (cone-bearing) Sequoias of temperate California, though deciduous trees can also grow huge in temperate forests. Northern forests consist mainly of conifers, pines, spruces and firs – some of them reach far beyond the arctic circle.

Felling in a softwood forest, using a specially built waterway; the logs shoot down this into the river, and float downstream

A nursery of young spruces grown from seed ready to plant out after two or three years' growth on an open hillside field

The trees are planted out on the hillside, with soil for growth, each in a separate wicker tub. Gradually the tubs rot away

As they grow, the decay of their fallen leaves makes more soil and by degrees the bare rocky slopes become covered with earth

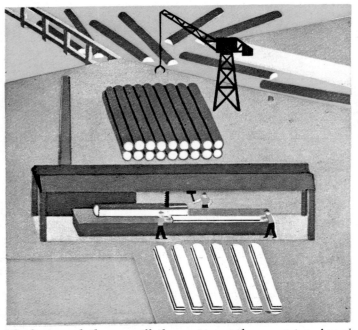

The logs reach the sawmill down river, and are cut into boards

Gaps are left and watch-towers built, to save the trees from fire

Tropical forests have resisted the advance of man for two main reasons: they are difficult to cut down and clear; and their climate is very hot and moist. But life can be comfortable for natives of tropical forest country once the hard work of cutting clearings is done, for crops grow quickly and easily. Disused clearings and forest paths rapidly grow over, though they always leave a trace, for the plants of the second growth are not quite the same as those of virgin forest. Much travel between places in tropical forests is by water or air, owing to the cost of land routes.

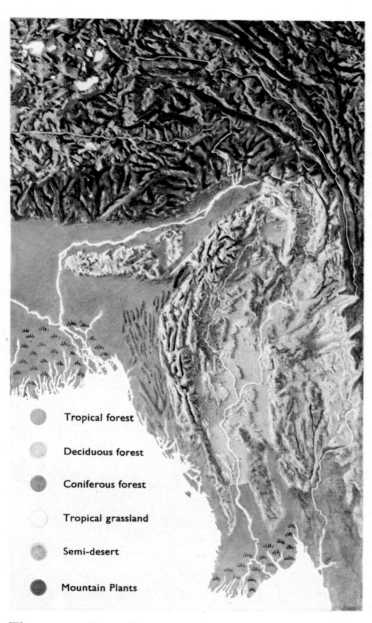

- Tropical forest
- Deciduous forest
- Coniferous forest
- Tropical grassland
- Semi-desert
- Mountain Plants

The maps show Burma, where teak-wood comes from. Quite different animals live at different levels; and people below know little of life in the tree-tops. Tropical forests are full of creepers, and plants that live on other plants, like orchids.

LIFE IN COLD COUNTRIES

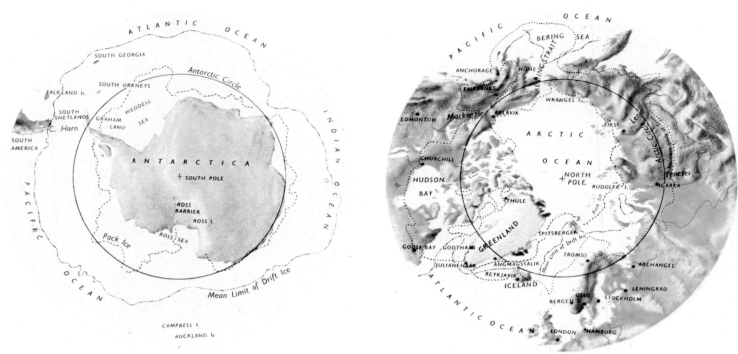

So far, man cannot wrest a living from the Antarctic Continent, but he has inhabited parts of the Arctic regions for centuries.

With ships like this powerful icebreaker, man can now keep both North-west and North-east Passages of the Arctic Ocean clear.

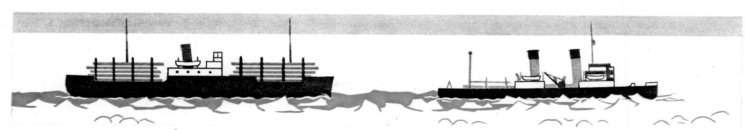

Lapps, in Arctic Europe, use reindeer to eat, give milk, provide skin and bone for tents, clothing and tools, and to drag their sledges.

Eskimos, in Arctic America, still build winter igloos of snow and hunt seals in kayaks, or harpoon them at their breathing-holes.

In Europe, Asia and North America thousands of people now make a living in truly Arctic regions, permanently frozen underground. They endure the long, cold, dark winter to manage mines, airfields, seaports, fisheries, meteorological stations, traplines, trading posts and missions.

Life in the Arctic is not all gloomy. The short summer is sunny, and in sheltered places there is a quick and quite thick growth of plants, as soon as the snow melts. Many kinds of flowers grow in carpets; and insects, even butterflies, visit them. Birds, like these guillemots or murres (on the cliff), snow-geese and phalaropes, come from the south to rear their young. The mammals are caribou (a big reindeer), walrus and polar bear, which usually do not wander so close to an Eskimo settlement. Some white explorers or traders have run up to the top of the plateau in a tracked vehicle. This scene is typical of parts of West Greenland, or the Canadian Arctic Archipelago; such as Baffin Land.

LIFE IN DESERTS

There are many areas of land on which few, or no, plants grow; the deserts. All the big ones are barren because they get scarcely any water; though some polar areas support no plants because they are too cold; others because no soil can form. Living things in deserts face lack of water, and great changes of temperature between day and night, and often between summer and winter. Many animals and desert men often travel and feed in the cool of the night. Wind-driven sandstorms are a danger to travellers, who also may be confused by mirages, illusions due to haze in the heat of the day. Most deserts are intersected by old or periodic watercourses which give the traveller some shelter and a hard track.

BARREN MOUNTAINS IN THE SAHARA

THE PAINTED DESERT IN ARIZONA

THE GREAT DESERT OF AUSTRALIA

DEATH VALLEY IN CALIFORNIA

THE COLD DESERT OF N. TIBET

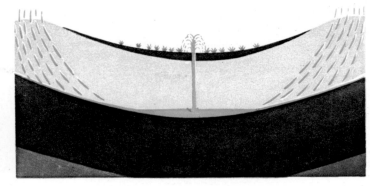

An oasis is an area of vegetation in a desert, which nearly always results from the presence of water. Water can be trapped where layers of rock are dipped and faulted (left), or folded to form a basin (right), and from this underground reservoir an oasis can be watered from wells. Sometimes, when water-carrying rock is sandwiched between two layers of water-resisting rock, a shaft makes an artesian well.

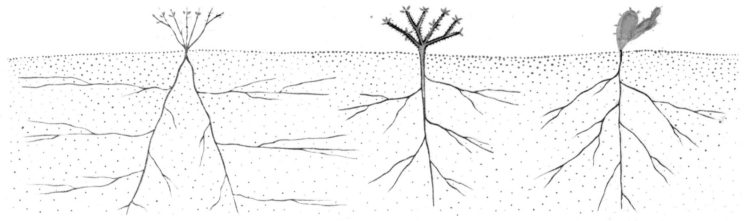

Desert plants find water by long roots, avoid evaporation with woody stems and narrow leaves, store water in stems and fleshy leaves.

The camel travels for days across the desert on the food in its hump, and the water which it stores in the pockets of its stomach.

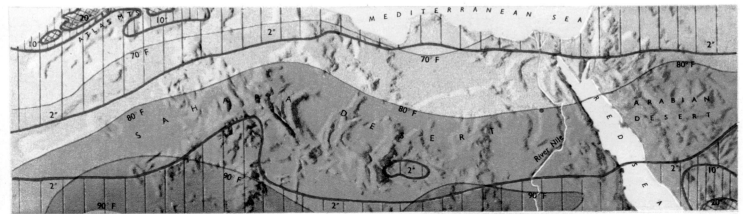

Most of the three million square miles of the Sahara have high temperatures and no rainfall; perhaps a storm every ten years. It is so vast that all France could fit into a part occupied only by sand. Most of it is dunes, and other areas are little but barren, stony wastes.

59

LIFE AT SEA

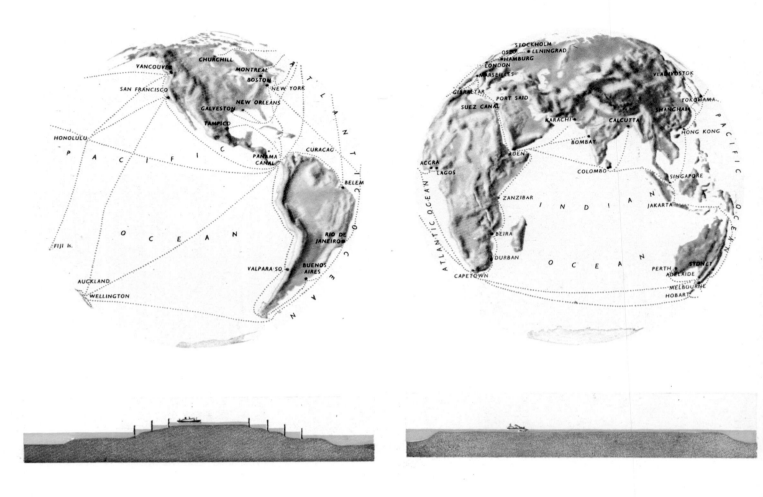

The sea covers seven tenths of the earth's surface; man uses it for trade, and as a source of food. Sea-trade became transformed in 1869, when the hundred-mile Suez Canal (right) was opened. It saves ships three weeks' time between London and India. In 1914 the Panama Canal (left) was opened; it is half the length of the Suez but, rising a hundred feet by locks, cost about seven times as much.

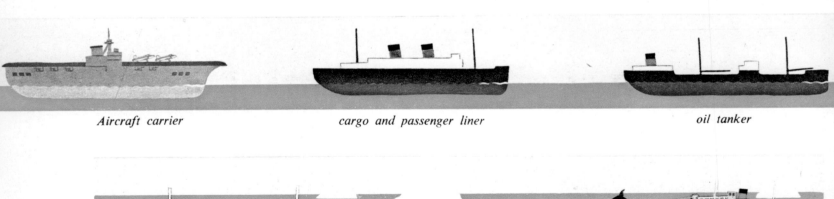

Aircraft carrier   *cargo and passenger liner*   *oil tanker*

Whaling in Antarctic seas.   An ever increasing proportion of the world's fats comes from the sea-mammals—mostly blue and fin-whales.

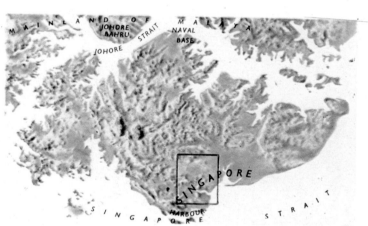

Man's seaports and dense human population grow by sheltered deep water. On the left is a map and picture of Rio de Janeiro, capital of Brazil, with its Sugar-loaf Mountain. Coffee, sugar and hides leave this port. Singapore, on the right, is the most important port in Asia; it was founded by the British in 1819 on a swamp. The map and picture show the town; the channel and mainland beyond.

sailing cargo-ship   *lightship towed by tug*   *cruiser*

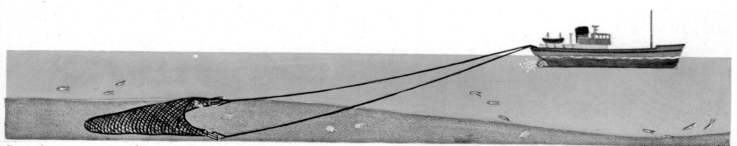

Soon the sea may provide man with as much food as the land; he has yet to exploit its small crustaceans and other possible resources.

MAN AND HIS FAITHS

The most densely populated areas are in Europe, India, China, Japan, Java and Egypt; in the rest of the world only the neighbourhood of big towns is crowded. Nearly all races of mankind are increasing, some faster than others. If this goes on, in time all the food the land produces will not be enough.

A simple map of world religions can show no faith truly, some not at all. The Jewish faith, for instance, is held by 11 million people over the world; and many Christians live in the area of 'others'.

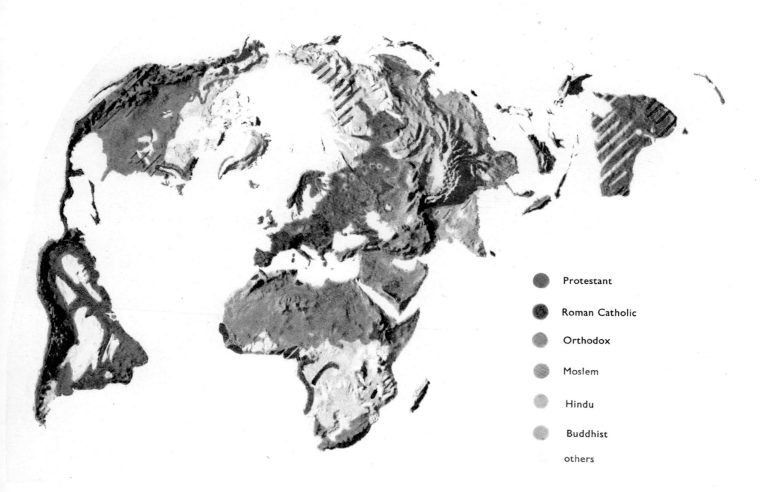

- Protestant
- Roman Catholic
- Orthodox
- Moslem
- Hindu
- Buddhist

others

Mecca, the holy city of the 200 million followers of Mohammed.

The first church of the Christian faith was built at Jerusalem.

In Lhasa, Tibet, and spreading throughout China and South East Asia, are 140 million Buddhists. India has over 200 million Hindus.

The teaching of Jesus Christ has a world-wide following of 700 million. The first church built in Europe was St. Peter's, Rome.

MAN AND THE UNKNOWN

Beginning in the Eastern Mediterranean, the story of the exploration of our earth gradually unrolls itself in these maps. It is from the Mediterranean that we can trace the growth of knowledge, the

150 A.D.

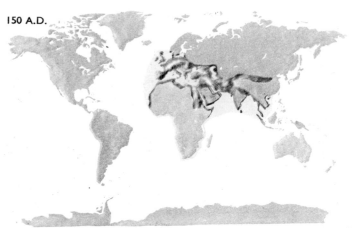

By about 150 the Roman Empire reached its utmost limits and its roads and walls spanned the 'known' world – for the existence of a greater civilization in China was almost as unknown to the Romans as were the growing civilizations of Central and South America.

1000 A.D.

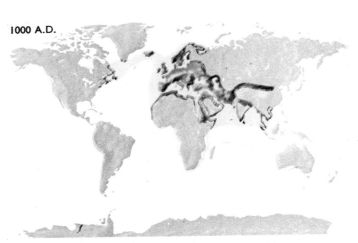

In long ships, the Vikings, the most daring sea-travellers of any age, colonized Iceland in 874, saw Greenland in 877 and colonized it in 986. They discovered North America possibly in 986, so that by 1000 the line of exploration is touching the New World.

1300 A.D.

In 1265 Nicolo and Maffeo Polo of Venice travelled to the Court of Kublai, Khakhan of the Mongols, in Peking; they returned in 1275 with Nicolo's son Marco, who wrote the famous story of adventure. In 1300 the known world included the Mongol Empire.

lines of exploration pointing like fingers to the unknown. Outside this hub there existed other civilizations in China, Central America and the Andes; but none of these peoples looked outwards or pushed onwards in the desire for exploration, expansion and conquest. It was only from the Mediterranean that the drive to discover was dynamic, eventually embracing the whole world.

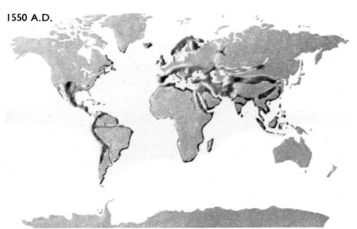

1550 A.D.

Columbus, in 1492, in search of a route to the riches of the East, sets foot in the West Indies, first in the New World since the Vikings. By 1550 the chief Old World nations were, each in turn, leading in exploration of a world now proved to be round.

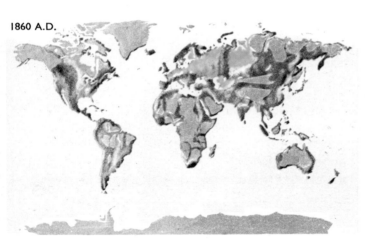

1860 A.D.

The period before 1860 saw many nations taking part in the exploration of the interior of each continent. The people of the temperate countries annexed most of the tropics. In Africa, Dr. Livingstone discovered the Victoria Falls on the Zambezi in 1855.

1910 A.D.

In the twentieth century nearly every last secret of the earth's surface has been unlocked. Amundsen reached the South Pole in 1911, and Captain Scott soon after. However, Antarctica is still the land of mystery in the south, as Greenland has remained in the north.

THE LAST SECRETS

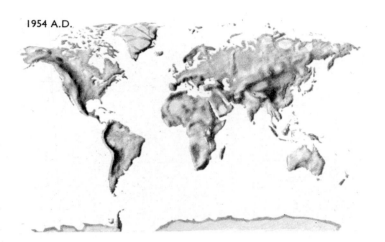

1954 A.D.

In May of 1953 Hillary and Tensing were first to climb Everest. Man has reached both Poles, and the top of the earth. There are some forests, tundras, icecaps and mountains that man has not explored; and he has only begun on the deep sea. But with machines he can get almost anywhere. No wonder he is dreaming of space, and believes that he can explore it. The imaginary picture shows a space-crew inspecting their ship near the moon. In the distance is a satellite station and another spaceship taking off. The first man to stand on the moon may already have been born in this generation.

Flying boats, parachuted supplies and tracked vehicles help arctic exploration.

In a pressure-proof "bathysphere", scientists make new discoveries in the deep.

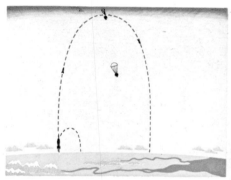

In a two-stage rocket, a robot observer can go 250 miles up, beyond atmosphere.

Printed in Great Britain by L.T.A. Robinson Ltd. London

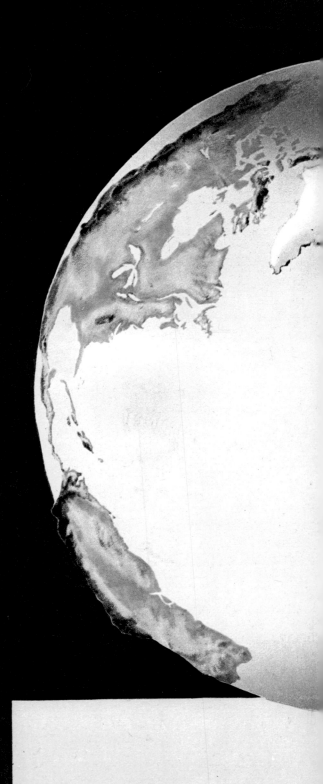

London is the middle of the map projection devise
by the late Professor Fawcett: this half of the glob
contains most of the land. The bits of the other ha
that contain important lands are 'peeled' back.

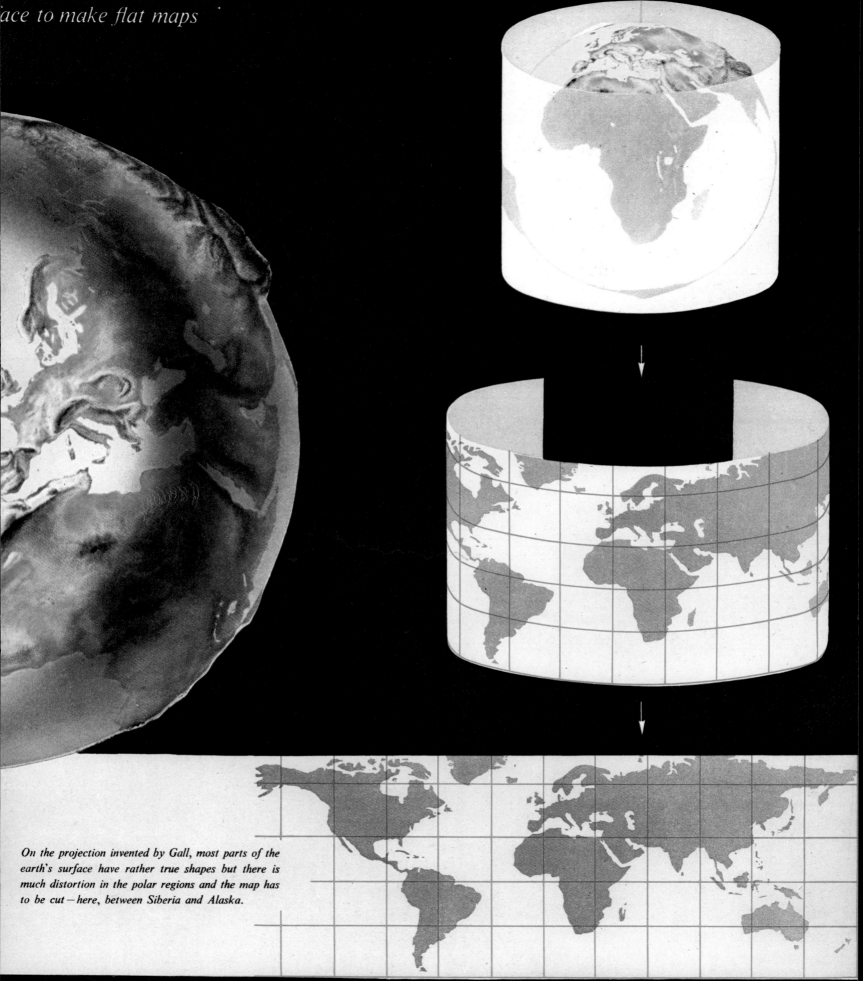

On the projection invented by Gall, most parts of the earth's surface have rather true shapes but there is much distortion in the polar regions and the map has to be cut—here, between Siberia and Alaska.

The Wonderful World OF THE SEA

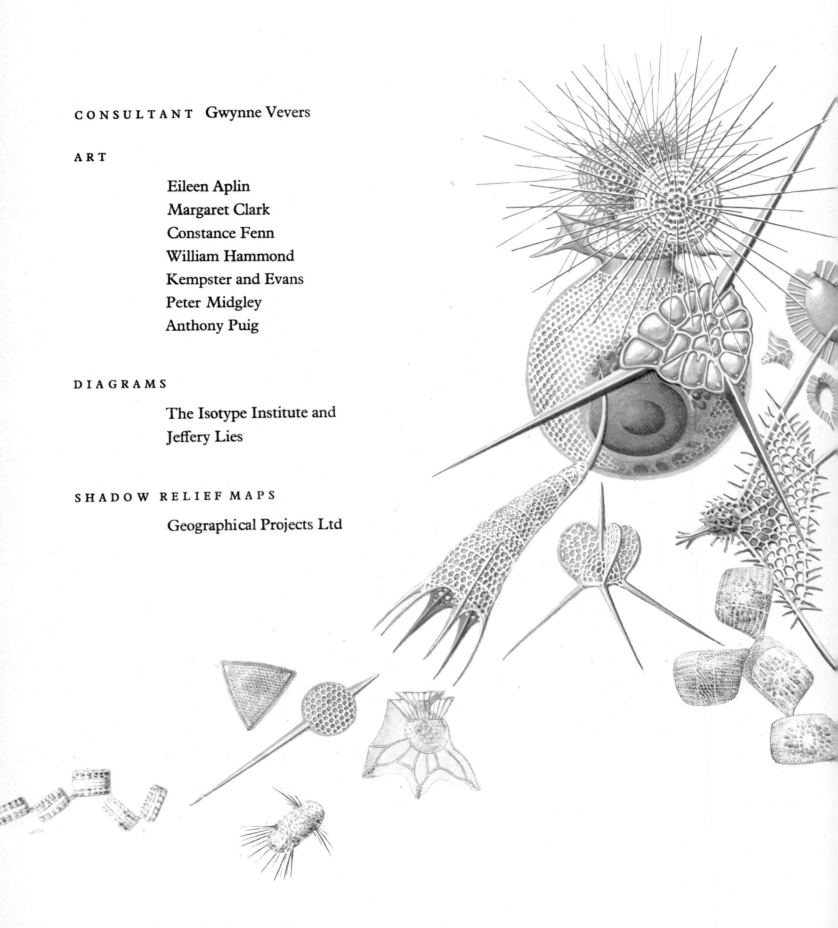

CONSULTANT   Gwynne Vevers

ART

    Eileen Aplin
    Margaret Clark
    Constance Fenn
    William Hammond
    Kempster and Evans
    Peter Midgley
    Anthony Puig

DIAGRAMS

    The Isotype Institute and
    Jeffery Lies

SHADOW RELIEF MAPS

    Geographical Projects Ltd

Library of Congress Card Catalog No. 57-5564

PRODUCED BY RATHBONE BOOKS, LONDON · PRINTED IN GREAT BRITAIN BY L. T. A. ROBINSON LIMITED, LONDON

The Wonderful World
OF THE SEA

James Fisher

CONTENTS

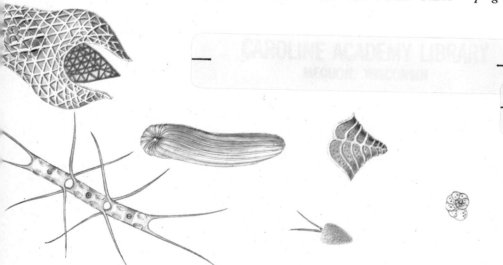

First published in the United States of America in 1957

GARDEN CITY BOOKS GARDEN CITY NEW YORK

The Sea and Its Waters

A WORLD WITHOUT A SEA is almost certainly a world without life. A planet or moon with no sea has a surface of lifeless rock, or rock and dust. Above that surface there may be no atmosphere at all; or there may be an atmosphere of poisonous gas, such as carbon dioxide, methane or ammonia.

Among the planets that belong to our sun, and the moons that belong to them, only a few have water on or above their surfaces; and apart from our own earth, only one has anything resembling a sea. For the range of temperature at which water exists in liquid form – the range between freezing point and boiling point – is quite small compared with the tremendous difference between the temperature of the coldest planet (probably Pluto) and the hottest (Mercury, on that side of it which is turned always towards the sun).

The rings of Saturn may be crystals of ice – solid water. The clouds around Venus probably consist mainly of carbon dioxide, but they may also contain water vapour. Mars alone may have a water system not unlike our own; it has ice-caps which grow and shrink with the seasons, vast expanses which are probably covered with sea, and possibly straight great ditches – the so-called 'canals' – which may also contain water.

Life may possibly exist on Venus, whose solid surface we cannot see. It probably exists on Mars. But it is very unlikely that it exists in the solar system on any other planet (except, of course, the earth) or on any moon. As we look at the face of our earth, with its rich land and fertile sea teeming with life, we can ponder, and wonder at the fact that once – perhaps 2,000 million years ago – our planet must have had a barren, sea-less surface like that of the moon.

The story of the seas and how from them came life; and from life, man; and in man, an understanding of the sea, is one of the greatest stories of nature and man – the Adventure of the Sea.

The oceaned earth, mother of teeming life

The waterless m barren and des

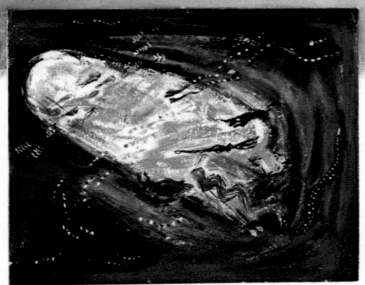

The greatest sea-depths, at six miles, are but wrinkles on the face of the earth. Diving spheres have explored only the middle depths.

From most directions, space-travellers approaching the earth would see far more water than land; from no angle would they see more land than water. Yet if our planet were the size of a grapefruit its seas and the air above them would be as thin as paper.

The whole surface of our earth has an area of about 197 million square miles. Of this, 141 million square miles, or a little over seven-tenths, are covered with water. If we could look at the earth from space, we could never find a half on which there is more land than water; but we could find one on which there is scarcely any land at all – the half which contains the Pacific Ocean. This great ocean occupies nearly a third of the earth's surface; the Atlantic Ocean and the slightly smaller Indian Ocean combined occupy almost another third.

Yet while the sea's area is vast, its depth is comparatively slight. The greatest ocean depths, like the highest mountains, are but tiny irregularities on the surface of the earth, which we could scarcely detect on a school globe were it made to scale in all

Everest, five-and-a-half miles high, shows as a slight irregularity on our earth's surface.
Mount Everest Foundation.

dimensions. Mount Everest's top is but twelve miles higher than the bottom of the Japan Trench, the world's deepest sea-area; and twelve miles is little more than one-and-a-half thousandths of the diameter of the earth.

Continually, through the ages, frost, wind and rain break up and destroy the land of the continents and islands, and the sea incessantly works at their cliffs and shores. This process is known as erosion, and its products, called sediments, are swept down by rivers and along by currents to form an apron which skirts the land. This apron is the continental shelf, and it slopes very gently out into the sea until it reaches a depth of about six hundred feet below its surface. In places the continental shelf may extend for hundreds of miles, as in Hudson's Bay, or around Newfoundland, or in the Baltic and North Seas and around Britain.

Beyond the continental shelf the sea-floor slopes more steeply, and for a great distance. This long slope, the continental slope, usually descends to a depth of two to three miles. Beyond this the ocean floor is so often flat, or nearly flat, that it has been called the Plain of the Abyss. No sediments from the land ever reach this plain. Instead, it is covered by 'oozes', which are the remains of the plants and smaller animals that live in the sea, and scattered with the harder parts of the skeletons of the larger animals that swim in it.

Only about a fiftieth of the area of the bottom of the sea is deeper than the Plain of the Abyss. Several of the 'trenches' plunge to a depth of more than four and a half miles. Most of them lie, rather interestingly, not far from the coasts of continents, or from chains of islands, in the western parts of the Atlantic and Pacific Oceans, and in the eastern part of the Indian Ocean.

The total volume of water that rests on the ocean-bed is 324 million cubic miles. This means that the volume of the sea is fourteen times as great as that of all the earth's dry land above sea-level. If the surface of the earth were perfectly smooth, the waters of the sea would flood the whole of it to a depth of about two miles.

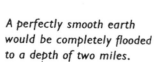

Average height of dry land is 2,500 feet. Average depth of sea is 14,200 feet.

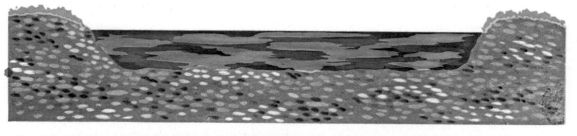

A perfectly smooth earth would be completely flooded to a depth of two miles.

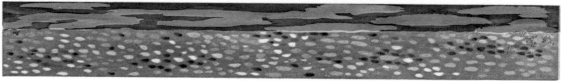

In the wind-swept Atlantic, waves often reach a height of thirty-five feet and a length from crest to crest of several hundred yards.

This colossal bulk of water is always moving. Waves, the most obvious form of motion, and currents, the most important to man, both spring from the wind.

Fasten one end of a rope and shake the other. Waves will travel along it; but each part of the rope will rise and fall – not move along itself. In almost the same way, every particle of water in a wave moves up and down much farther than it moves along. When the wind is in the same direction as the surface current, the water moves with it, but comparatively slowly; when it is not, the water may even move in a direction opposite to that of the waves.

When a wind blows over the surface of a smooth sea, small waves appear: we are not certain just how they do so. But once they have been aroused they grow quickly under the pressure of the wind. Atlantic gales often produce waves thirty-five vertical feet from trough to crest, and have been known to raise rollers up to fifty feet high. These big storm-waves are sometimes a quarter of a mile from crest to crest. The longest ever recorded was about seven-tenths of a mile.

Perhaps 'wave' is the wrong word, for we have come to use it to mean a breaker on a beach, or a sea-wave whose top curls over in a flurry of white water. 'White-horses', as such sea-waves are called, are seen only when high winds overturn the crests, and are unusual if the distance between crests is more than seven times the height of the waves. A wave system may be deep and long, yet never break: such a system is called a swell. Huge swells may travel right across the Atlantic, thousands of miles away from the storm or the gale in which they were born.

The main currents of the sea are closely connected with the prevailing winds – those winds which, over large areas of the earth, maintain roughly the same direction throughout the greater part of the year.

In the tropics the midday sun is high overhead. There, much more than in the temperate and polar regions, its rays penetrate the atmosphere and heat the surface of land and sea. The air is thus heated at the bottom; and hot air, being less dense than cool air, rises. To replace this rising air, cooler air flows in from north and south towards the equator. As it flows, the eastward spin of the earth deflects it towards the west.

In the tropics, then, the prevailing winds blow from the east. In the temperate zones the returning air circulates and the prevailing winds are westerly. Although not all sea scientists have agreed in the past, it is now generally believed that the great surface currents of the oceans are aroused by these prevailing winds, and get their energy from them.

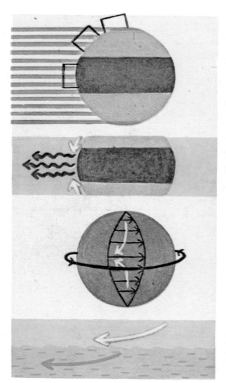

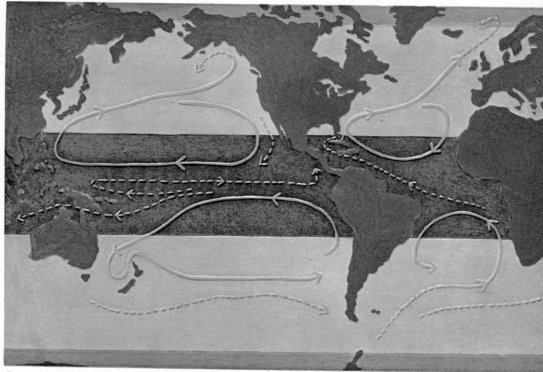

Hot, light tropical air rises. Cool air flowing in from north and south is deflected westward by the earth's spin.

Prevailing winds in the tropics thus blow from the east. In temperate regions the return circulation causes prevailing westerly winds. From prevailing winds, enough energy is transferred to the sea's waters to produce the main ocean currents.

These great currents dominate the seas, and the circulation of the waters everywhere springs from them. When we go into detail, of course, we find that the whole system is very complicated, though its broad pattern changes rather little with time and season. At the boundary of every ocean we find the currents deflected by the continental slopes. In the middle of the Pacific, almost on the equator, flows an east-going counter-current between the two typical west-going tropical streams. Many counter-currents, usually differing in temperature from those above, flow far *below*, and in directions sometimes opposed to the main surface currents.

Often two currents, one cold, the other warm, converge along a sharp line, easily visible on the sea-surface and noticeable by the sudden change in temperature and in animal and plant life. There is such a marked convergence off the coast of Newfoundland, Nova Scotia and New England, where the cold Labrador Current meets the warm Gulf Stream. There is another around the Antarctic Ocean, where the cold polar water sinks below the warmer seas of the southern oceans, and – within a mile – the temperature of the sea-surface may change by as much as eight degrees Fahrenheit.

Centuries ago, Pacific-Islanders made use of prevailing currents to speed their ocean-crossings.

12

At St. John, Bay of Fundy, a low tide almost drains this basin.
New Brunswick Government Information Bureau

High tide, adding over twenty feet to the water-level, brims it.

Tides, the regular rhythm of the sea, are caused by the pull which the moon and sun exert on the earth. Matter attracts all other matter with a force that depends on its amount, or mass, and its distance. The greater the mass, the greater the pull; the greater the distance, the *smaller* the pull. The moon has less than an eightieth of the earth's mass and

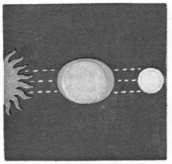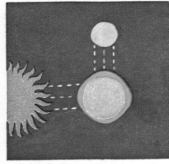

Sun and moon pulling in line produce maximum or spring tides; pulling at right-angles they produce minimum or neap tides.

is less than a quarter of a million miles from it; its pull on the earth is strong. The sun with a mass over a third of a million times that of the earth's is some 93 million miles away; its pull is weaker.

The earth attracts its own waters with a force millions of times greater than that of moon and sun. Yet their pull is enough to draw the ocean waters into a pile. This pile is a wave which, in the open ocean, follows beneath the revolving moon. It is the true tidal wave – quite a different thing from the so-called 'tidal waves' which may appear after volcanic disturbances on the sea-bed.

The length of the tidal wave must be measured in hours rather than in distance. It is about twelve hours and twenty minutes long – just half the time it takes for the moon to circle the earth; for each tidal wave on the side of the earth nearest the moon is balanced by another on the opposite side.

The height of the tidal wave is known as the tidal range. In the broad oceans, the tidal wave is about three feet high and travels at roughly five hundred miles an hour. Oceanic islands thus have small tides; the range at the Azores, for instance, is only about five feet. Across the shallows of continental shelves, and in enclosed seas, the tidal wave is slowed down by friction, and as it slows it deepens. The greatest known tidal range in the world is in the Bay of

Julius Caesar, unused to large tides, beached his ships on the east coast of Kent. A twenty-foot spring tide and a following wind left his fleet high and dry.

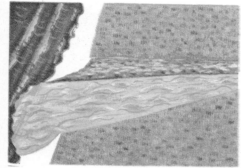

Where a river-estuary narrows rapidly . . .

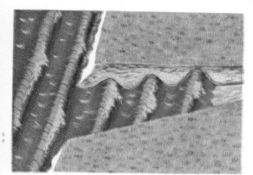

tides sometimes build up to great heights.

At high spring tide, a wall of water – a bore – rushes up the Hoogly River, in India.

Fundy, in eastern North America. Half-way up this bay, at St. John, the tidal range averages over twenty feet; at its head, at Noel Bay, it averages over forty-four. Spring tides in Noel Bay bring a rise and fall of over fifty feet. Among other coasts with ranges of over twenty feet are those of north France, south-west England and parts of Mexico and Australia.

At new moon and full moon, the pull of sun and moon are added to each other, and the tidal range is at its greatest. Tides at this time are known as spring tides. At half moon, the pulls of sun and moon are opposed, and the tides, then called neap tides, are smallest.

Many early voyagers got into trouble when they met big tides for the first time. Julius Caesar, whose legions invaded Britain in 55 B.C., was accustomed to the small tides of the Mediterranean. His main fleet was beached between Walmer and Deal, and left high and dry by a twenty-foot spring tide, backed by a strong wind. Many ships were put out of action, and only with a struggle were the experienced and heavily-armed Roman soldiers able to defeat the ill-equipped Britons.

When a spring tide is reinforced by a strong, continuous gale the waters may climb to an unexpected height in what is called a surge. In 1953 great surges drowned over a thousand people on the coasts of England and Holland, and in Scotland fishing boats were torn from their anchorage and stranded far above normal high-water mark.

In 1953, spring tides backed by gales brought havoc to the Dutch and British coasts. In Loch Broom, Scotland, large boats were stranded far above normal high-tide mark.

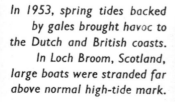

East Indies: Here the volcanic island of Krakatoa blew itself to pieces. Within minutes, millions of tons of rock hurtled into the sea.

Constantly the ocean wears away and shifts the edge of the land. Constantly rivers carry silt down to the sea. Occasionally rock and dust are hurled into the sea by volcanic action. It is from these sources that the waters gain a gradual increase in their wealth of minerals.

In the Sunda Strait, between Java and Sumatra, there was once a volcanic island, Krakatoa. It had an area of about eighteen square miles, and rose to a height of a quarter of a mile. In August, 1883, it blew up, in one of the most tremendous volcanic eruptions in history. For two days violent explosions blasted rocks, lava and ash seventeen miles and more into the air. Volcanic dust darkened the skies a hundred miles away and heightened the tints of sunrise and sunset in most parts of the world for several months afterwards.

When the eruption was over, a great gash over a thousand feet deep was left in the sea-bed and a wide area of the surrounding sea-floor was covered with a deep layer of debris. A group of new islands was formed near by.

The explosions also generated a succession of giant waves, as much as fifty feet high, which caused terrible destruction throughout the East Indies. More than thirty-six thousand people were drowned.

Some of these waves could be detected at Cape Horn, nearly half-way round the world.

Fortunately the edge of the sea is not very often changed by volcanic disturbances. Nearly all the coastal scenery that we find throughout the world looks as it does because of the slow but relentless work of waves and tides.

When waves break upon a shore their very weight is enough to shift some solid matter; but the main instruments of sea erosion are the stones, gravel and sand which the breakers carry up from the shore and

East Anglia: In a few hours, high seas swallowed acres of cliff.
Geological Survey and Museum, London

cast upon beach or cliff. So great is the hammering power of the stone- or sand-laden waves that in parts of the world where the cliffs are soft, such as the east of England, the work of the sea can be quite rapid. Yorkshire was occupied by the Romans less than two thousand years ago, and we know that since then parts of its coast have lost as much as two miles to the sea. During a tidal surge, the sea may bite off large chunks of soft cliff in a few hours. In East Anglia, for instance, there was a very high spring tide and a surge on 30th November, 1939. Just south of Lowestoft many tons of cliff fell into the sea and houses were left tottering on the broken cliff-edge.

Where cliffs are of hard rock, the patient ocean works more slowly. It has taken millions of years for the waves to chisel and carve the hard coast of California into the rugged cliffs and natural rock-arches that we see today. On these hard coasts, the sea, laden with pieces of rock that it has already torn from the shore, works by under-cutting.

Nowhere in the North Atlantic is the scenery of cliff-cutting more noble than at St. Kilda and its neighbouring islands, west of the Outer Hebrides in Scotland. Here the island of Boreray has sheer cliffs a quarter of a mile high, and others nearly as high which actually overhang.

Boreray, the world's largest nesting-place of gannets, is formed of an exceptionally hard kind of rock, known as gabbro, and the sea works on it so slowly that scarcely any changes have been noted in hundreds of years of human observation. But the period during which human beings have lived on St. Kilda is but a tiny span compared with the millions of years in which the raging Atlantic has been battering, under-cutting and sculpting its terrible precipices.

California: Slowly, relentlessly, the sea has breached solid rock.

Boreray: Millions of years of Atlantic swell
have undercut rocks among the hardest on earth.

16 The sea steals land from many coasts, but brings new shores to many others. For a thousand million years or more sea and land have changed their positions and distribution. The earth's crust has warped and buckled; different parts of it at different times have been subjected to heavy stress. Sometimes, at the edge of an ocean, the weight of a great land-mass has pressed downward; compensating upward movements of the ocean floor have raised new islands and lands within the sea.

We know that through the long ages the continents have changed tremendously in shape. Vast areas which were once continental shelves, covered with sediments brought down into the sea from the land's rivers, have later become raised above sea-

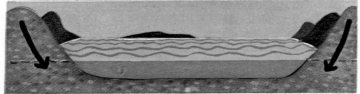

When the weight of land-masses press down at the ocean-edge . . .

the sea-floor may buckle and raise up new islands from the sea.

level, and folded and pushed into mountain ranges. The top of Mount Everest, which is composed of limestone, was once part of a sediment at the bottom of the sea.

Some people think that the main continental masses have been much the same throughout geological history; although, of course, their shapes have changed as land-masses rose above or fell below sea-level. Others think that 500 million years ago the continents were all grouped together in one great

Under the Pacific, volcanic activity may suddenly raise new islands, which are colonised and broadened by coral.

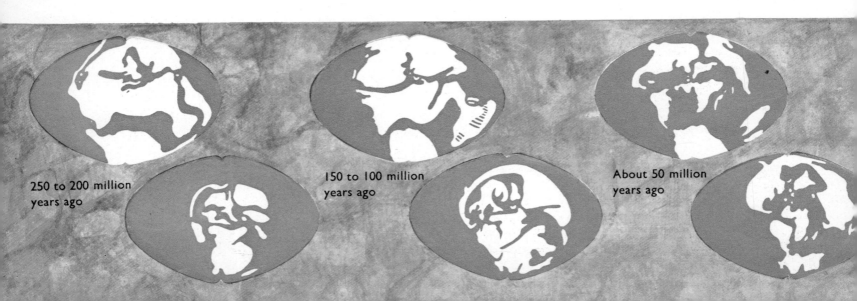

250 to 200 million years ago

150 to 100 million years ago

About 50 million years ago

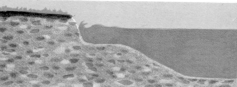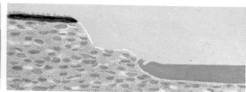

Over long years waves and tide wear a shelving beach at the foot of a coastal hill. When the land-mass lifts, a raised beach is formed.

land-mass, and that this mass split into pieces which very gradually drifted apart until they reached their present positions. Few geographers would care to say, on the evidence at present available, which of these theories is right.

Lesser and more recent changes we can follow rather more surely. Many of them are due to the redistribution of weight on the land. For instance, when a land-mass is covered with heavy sheets of ice it presses down on the liquid layers below the earth's crust; it sinks a little into those layers and pushes up the sea-floor elsewhere. Afterwards, when the ice melts, this pressure is released and the land-mass rises again out of the sea. In arctic lands we can sometimes clearly see that this has happened. With the melting of the ice-caps since the last Ice Age (that is, in the last fifteen thousand years or so) some parts of these lands have risen far out of the sea: we can now detect, well inland, old sea beaches a hundred feet or more above the present level of the sea.

Raised beach in Spitsbergen, formed when the last Ice Age ended.

Alterations in the distribution of land weight may result in volcanic action. In the Pacific, particularly, new islands have occasionally appeared as a result of submarine volcanic disturbance. Such new land is quickly colonised by corals, and extended by the gradual accumulation of their tiny dead skeletons.

The great changes due to shifts in land weight and volcanic activity provide new coasts for waves and tides to work on. The sea pounds these coasts into sand, takes the sand away from one region, and drives it to another. Along some coasts, wind and tide work mainly in one direction: gravel and sand is driven into bars and ridges which often contain a calm lagoon between them and the mainland. When such bars are colonised by vegetation the lagoon may become silted and dry up. Outside the new land that has been formed in this way the process of ridge-building may begin all over again.

A sand-bar off America's east coast – the work of wind and tide.

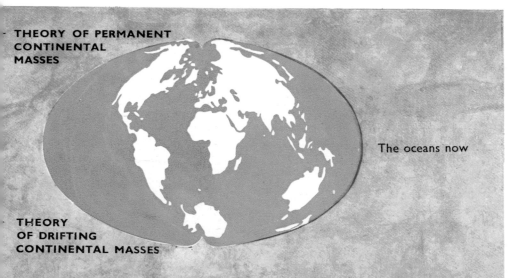

THEORY OF PERMANENT CONTINENTAL MASSES

The oceans now

THEORY OF DRIFTING CONTINENTAL MASSES

The true history of the oceans through the years may be told one day, when science has advanced further. At present only the crudest sketch-maps can be made of what the boundaries of land and sea may have been: and a set is necessary for each of the two principal theories.

On the maps in each set we must imagine new land forming by the deposit of sediments in the enclosed seas.

Minute single-celled
sea-plants, greatly enlarged

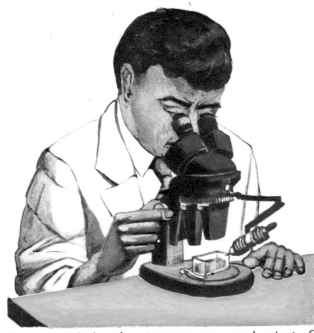

The marine biologist's microscope can reveal a host of
tiny animals (opposite) of fantastic, complex beauty.

The Sea and Its Life

WHEN OUR EARTH was about half its present age, some 1,000 million years ago, the first living things appeared in the sea. Nobody knows quite how this happened, how non-life turned into life.

This much is certain: before the dawn of life the waters of the sea were full of many salts, of compounds of many different elements. These chemical compounds, especially in the upper fifty fathoms of water, were subjected to various influences, including the heat and light of the sun. Under these influences one compound reacted with another; atoms of different elements combined with one another to form new and more complex compounds.

The simplest living things we know today are viruses. Some are so small that they cannot be seen under an ordinary microscope which can magnify about two thousand times. Yet scientists have closely studied some of them, and know that they are, in fact, extremely complicated compounds. Perhaps the first living matter much resembled a virus.

Almost certainly it had the power to feed – to take simpler substances from the water around it and turn them into the more complicated matter of which it was itself made.

At some unknown time some of these first living things became even more complex. They possessed a green compound known as chlorophyll which enabled them, in sunlight, to take water and carbon dioxide gas from sea or atmosphere, turn them into food, and release oxygen as a kind of by-product. They were the first true single-celled plants. Over an immense period of time some living things gradually lost the ability to make their own food, but gained the ability to live by eating plants. These were the first tiny animals to live on the earth.

It is a sub-tropical night with no moon. Myriads of luminous single-celled plants and animals swarm near the surface, lighting up the sea.

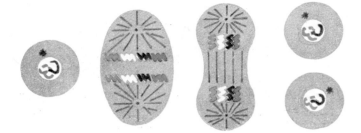

A single cell normally splits into two identical daughter-cells.

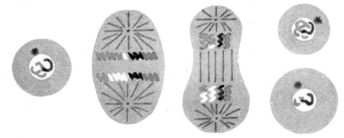

When chromosomes divide unevenly, daughter-cells are different.

Today there are over a million kinds of plants and animals. We shall never know in detail how all these have descended from one form, or possibly a few forms, of life. But we can find a clue by looking at some of the single-celled creatures which live now.

Inside a living cell all is not the same. Each contains a kind of inner core, or nucleus. Within the nucleus are bodies which we can see under the microscope: the chromosomes. When the cell reaches a certain stage of growth the chromosomes divide evenly and drift to opposite sides of the cell. Next, the nucleus itself splits into two, each containing a set of chromosomes. Finally the whole cell divides, forming two daughter-cells. Each of the two daughter-cells, if healthy, continues to grow, and usually

it becomes identical with the original parent-cell.

Sometimes the chromosomes do not divide quite equally, or tiny changes occur in their shape and composition. When this happens, the two daughter-cells are different from each other. Now when a stock of creatures of one kind begins to vary, it is likely that some will be better suited than others to survive in the struggle for life, and will have a better chance to grow and to divide. Any variation which is an improvement is more likely to be passed on to the next generation than one which is not.

Quite early in evolution's long story, some single cells did not separate on splitting: instead, they remained connected together as colonies, within which each cell still fed itself much as if it were living alone. Many seaweeds have this scheme of life, for joined together, their cells can float on the surface of the sea where there is plenty of sunlight to enable them to make their own food.

From simple colonies of identical cells, more complicated colonies evolved in which different cells began to specialise. Fossils from early rocks show that the animals that we call sponges existed more than 500 million years ago. In a sponge, some kinds of cells build the tough skeleton which covers the whole colony, some produce currents which carry food-particles to the main body-cells, and others are used in reproduction.

The coelenterates have progressed yet further. Their cells have become grouped in layers, and within each layer different cells have different tasks. One of the simplest animals of this group, the sea-

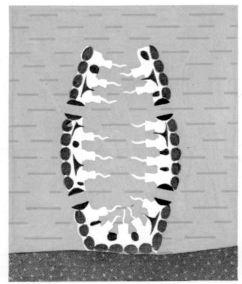
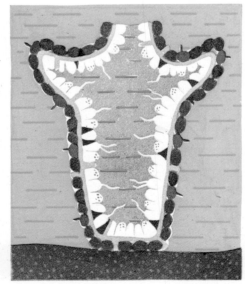

In most seaweeds, all cells are alike and all are self-supporting. In sponges, individual cells specialise – some building the skeleton, some producing food-carrying currents, others feeding. In the sea-anemone there are layers of cells, each with a specialist job.

anemone, is made up of a tough outer layer of cells, which protects it, and a soft inner layer, which digests its food; special cells form muscles, and others make up a simple net of nerves.

Some coelenterates carry specialisation further still. *Velella*, the by-the-wind-sailor, for instance, is made up of several colonies or polyps. Some encase the animal, some form stings, others make up a digestive system, while yet others form the sail which propels this strange living craft across the surface of the waters.

Among the simple animals of the sea we can trace many different kinds of evolution. The worms have developed specialised blood vessels, mouths, digestive tracts and nerve systems. Quite early in their evolution some worms became segmented. At first the segments, or divisions, were all much alike, but later they acquired different forms and different jobs. With these developments the worms can behave in quite complicated ways. Tube-worms, for instance, use sand and their own body-slime to build a firm, hard tube to live in. They catch food by means of feelers which protrude from the top. When threatened by enemies some can withdraw completely into the tube and seal the end with a plug.

All these sea animals are drawn to roughly life-size.
Top: by-the-wind-sailors; Right: jellyfish, sycon sponges
and sea-anemones; Bottom: tube-worms and sea-mouse.

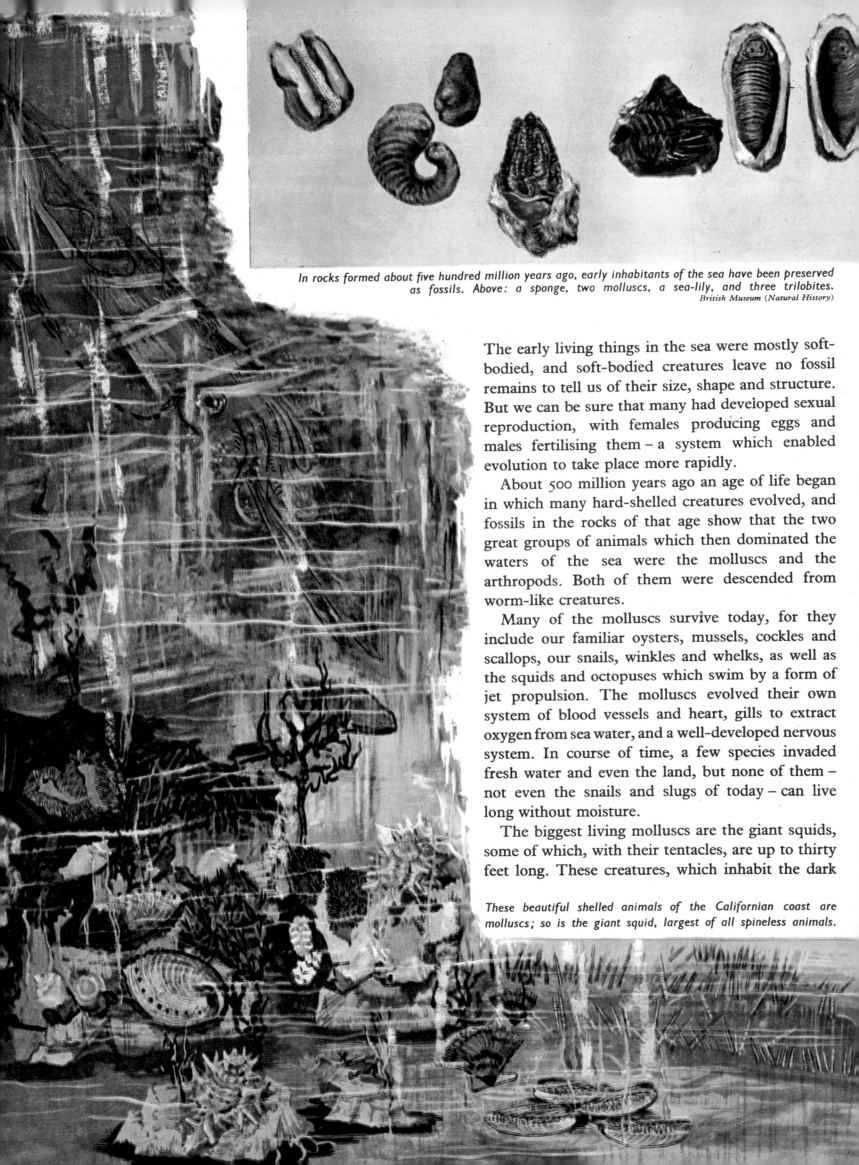

In rocks formed about five hundred million years ago, early inhabitants of the sea have been preserved as fossils. Above: a sponge, two molluscs, a sea-lily, and three trilobites.
British Museum (Natural History)

The early living things in the sea were mostly soft-bodied, and soft-bodied creatures leave no fossil remains to tell us of their size, shape and structure. But we can be sure that many had developed sexual reproduction, with females producing eggs and males fertilising them – a system which enabled evolution to take place more rapidly.

About 500 million years ago an age of life began in which many hard-shelled creatures evolved, and fossils in the rocks of that age show that the two great groups of animals which then dominated the waters of the sea were the molluscs and the arthropods. Both of them were descended from worm-like creatures.

Many of the molluscs survive today, for they include our familiar oysters, mussels, cockles and scallops, our snails, winkles and whelks, as well as the squids and octopuses which swim by a form of jet propulsion. The molluscs evolved their own system of blood vessels and heart, gills to extract oxygen from sea water, and a well-developed nervous system. In course of time, a few species invaded fresh water and even the land, but none of them – not even the snails and slugs of today – can live long without moisture.

The biggest living molluscs are the giant squids, some of which, with their tentacles, are up to thirty feet long. These creatures, which inhabit the dark

These beautiful shelled animals of the Californian coast are molluscs; so is the giant squid, largest of all spineless animals.

depths of the sea, are not only the largest, but also among the fastest, of all animals without backbones.

The group of arthropods, or jointed-legged animals, contains today more members than all the rest of the animal kingdom put together. Besides the crustaceans of the sea and fresh water, such as lobsters, crabs, shrimps and barnacles, it includes the spiders, the scorpions, the insects – the most numerous of the conquerors of the land – and several other classes of animals.

The earliest arthropods to become masters of the sea were the trilobites, whose jointed segments gave them an armour-like defence against enemies and yet enabled them to swim quickly through the water, or crawl swiftly over the sea-bed. Yet, efficient as they were in their time, all the trilobites are now extinct. They could not compete with the improved forms of animal life that evolved soon after them. These included not only the crustaceans, but also the echinoderms, or spiny-skinned animals, such as the beautiful, bright, symmetrical star-fishes, brittle-stars, sea-lilies and sea-urchins we know today.

The echinoderms and some of their allies had, and still have, tiny free-swimming young ones: larvae. From these, or from creatures resembling them, animals with an entirely new kind of body structure arose. These animals, the vertebrates, or backboned animals, were gradually beginning to take over the mastery of the sea at the end of the first age of fossils, about 250 million years ago.

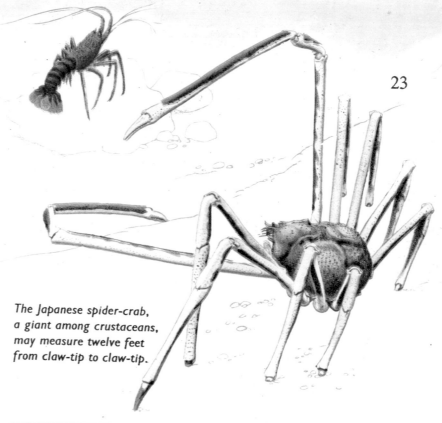

The Japanese spider-crab, a giant among crustaceans, may measure twelve feet from claw-tip to claw-tip.

British echinoderms: sea-urchins, star-fishes and brittle-stars.

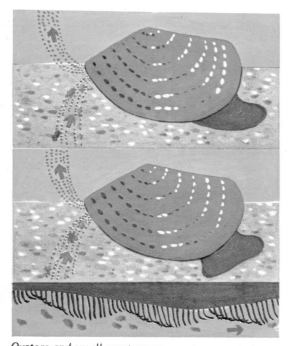
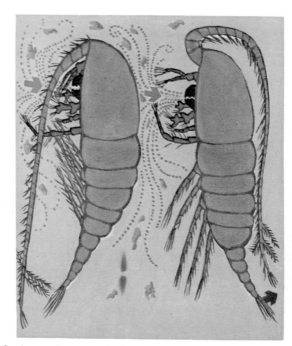
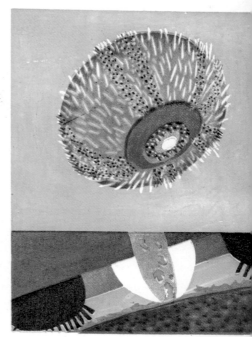

Oysters and small crustaceans create currents to carry food particles towards them. The sea-urchin has 'teeth' and can bite weed from the rocks.

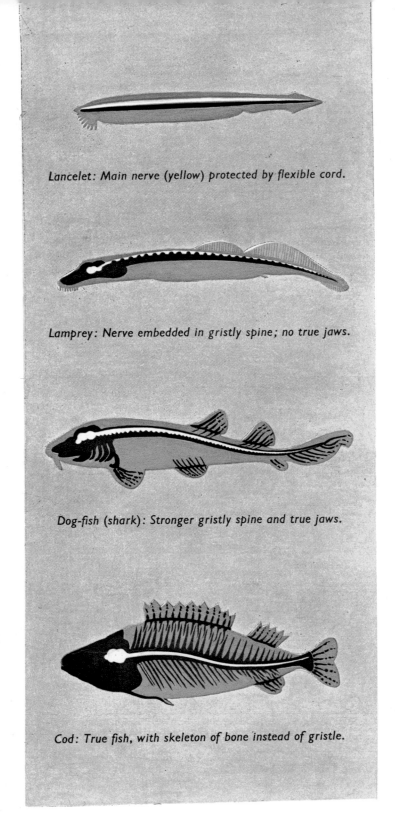

Lancelet: *Main nerve (yellow) protected by flexible cord.*

Lamprey: *Nerve embedded in gristly spine; no true jaws.*

Dog-fish (shark): *Stronger gristly spine and true jaws.*

Cod: *True fish, with skeleton of bone instead of gristle.*

The mud-skipper lives – and sees – equally well in water or out.

Animals with stiffened backs, not unlike lancelets, first appeared in the sea 400 million years ago or more. Soon they grew more complicated and passed through a stage resembling the modern lamprey. Next came animals with true jaws and skeletons made of gristle. The first true fishes, in which gristle is replaced by bone, evolved some 300 million years ago. The bony fishes and their more primitive gristly relations, such as the sharks, skates and rays, are still the dominant form of life in the sea. Well over twenty thousand species of living fish are known

today, and marine biologists are still discovering new ones every year.

In the course of their long domination of the waters, the fishes have made several experiments in the colonisation of the land. That these experiments still go on can readily be realised by anybody who meets a mud-skipper in a mangrove swamp. This fish, like nearly all others, breathes by means of gills, and when it climbs about the mangrove out of water it must still stay moist to live. But not long after the first true fishes evolved, one group developed lungs which enabled them to be independent of water for months at a time. Some of these lunged fishes had fins which evolved into primitive limbs with which they shuffled about the land, and soon true amphibians were established on the earth.

Today fishes range in size from tiny tropical fresh-water creatures a quarter of an inch long to giant whale-sharks, fifty feet long and weighing many tons. In the greatest depths of the ocean live incredible caricatures of fish, all head and jaws with fearsome teeth; at the surface of tropical seas, flying fish, pursued by their enemies, dash out of the waves and glide a hundred yards on broad wings – their highly developed pectoral fins. There are fish with poisonous spines; fish with snouts like swords; fish that can inflate themselves to twice their normal size; flattened fish, like rays and halibut, elongated fish, like pikes and eels; fish that attach themselves to rocks, or even to other fish, with suckers.

Flying fish: the 'wings' are fins.

From the picture below we can see something of the wide diversity of fish in one small area of the warm rock and coral shore of South Africa. At the top are five box-fish, curious creatures with hard body armour. Below them, just in front of the big blue-eye skate, swim two tobies, or Moorish idols. When native fishermen catch one they bow to it and return it carefully to the water. Above the sea-horses is a scorpion-fish, or sting-fish, whose body is covered with poisonous slime. The two snake-like fishes are both Moray eels, extremely aggressive fish for their size, and a danger to divers. Between them swim a couple of handsome coral fish. To the right of the larger eel is a fireworks-fish, or devil-fish; to the left swim three small gobies, and above them a large rainbow-fish. When the rainbow-fish is caught its body quickly fades to peacock blue.

Pilot-fishes follow sharks as jackals follow lions.

There are over 20,000 species of fish. Here, off the South African coast, we see something of their diversity of size, shape and coloration.

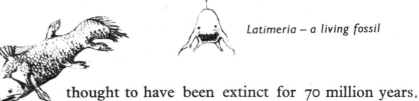

26

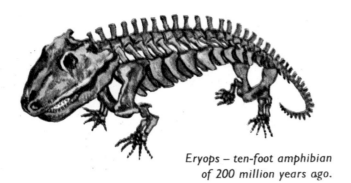

Eryops – ten-foot amphibian of 200 million years ago.

The fish made their first trials in colonising the land about 280 million years ago, when the great coal-forests flourished. One of the early orders of fishes which took part in these experiments survives to this day, for a handful of lung-fish still lives in the waters of Africa, Australia and South America. But it seems likely that the backboned animals of the land are descended from a different, though related, order of primitive fishes closer to the Coelacanths. The fossil record of the rocks shows that these creatures lived in the waters of the seas from 300 to 70 million years ago. Imagine, then, the surprise of zoologists when, in 1939, a live Coelacanth was caught off the coast of South Africa. This species, *Latimeria*, is still the only known living representative of an order once

Paddle-limbed plesiosaurs swam the seas some 150 million years ago.

Other sea-reptiles of this and earlier periods were the fish-shaped ichthyosaurs.
British Museum (Natural History)

thought to have been extinct for 70 million years.

From fishes which must have closely resembled our living fossil, *Latimeria*, with its limb-like fins, the first amphibians evolved. For a long time they spent part of their lives (especially the growing stages) in the water, as frogs do. But in time some became independent of water for all stages of their life-history. Then they were able to evolve quite rapidly, and over 200 million years ago they gave rise to the first reptiles. For the next 130 million years reptiles, including many giant dinosaurs, were the dominant forms of backboned life on the land.

They were so successful that it is not surprising that some of them returned to the sea and continued their evolution there. Great fish-shaped ichthyosaurs, true reptiles, appeared in the open seas nearly 200 million years ago. These splendid swimmers brought forth their young alive. In rocks 150 million years old we find remains of a different, very long-necked group of sea-reptiles, the plesiosaurs. Somewhat later came giant turtles and reptiles like great sea-serpents, the mosasaurs. Not many sea-reptiles survive today: there are still a few sea snakes in shallow waters, but the only reptiles now living in the open ocean are the heavily armoured turtles.

More successful in their return to the seas were the mammals. The earliest mammals probably evolved from reptiles. For many millions of years these creatures, which could control their own temperature and nourish their growing young within themselves, evolved side-by-side with the reptiles. But 70 million years ago there came great changes in the climate of the earth and major upheavals of

One of the few sea-reptiles of today – a turtle.

the sea-bed. Quickly many of the great reptiles died out and were supplanted by the more adaptable mammals. In place of the ichthyosaurs, plesiosaurs and mosasaurs came two groups of mammals adapted for life in the sea: the whales and the sea-cows. Few members of the sea-cow group now survive, but the whales are the greatest animals of modern seas. Indeed, the largest of them, the blue whale, may weigh a hundred tons, and is the largest animal that has ever existed upon the face of the earth.

The latest of the mammals to take to a marine life are the sea-otters and the seals. The seals, though very successful travellers in, and exploiters of, the open ocean, still have to return to its shores to breed. Every spring, the northern fur-seals of the Pacific land on the beaches of the Pribilof Islands, in the Bering Sea. When their young are born, in mid-summer, the islands support one and three-quarter million seals, the greatest gathering of large mammals of one kind found anywhere in the world.

We can be sure that there were birds adapted to sea life 100 million years ago. Today there are about 8,600 species of birds, and of these not much more than 200 are truly birds of the ocean. But though ocean birds are comparatively few, they have mastered the whole of the sea from pole to pole.

Each spring the northern fur-seals land on the beaches of the Pribilof Islands, Alaska, to breed. Each 'beach-master' (adult bull) has its own territory and its own harem.

1. Gentoo penguin: swift underwater swimmer. 2. Herring-gull: soars and scavenges over shallow water. 3. Cormorant: swims with wings and feet. 4. Gannet: dives on fish from a height. 5. Frigate-bird: most agile flyer of the seas. 6. Fulmar: dynamic soarer, ranges hundreds of miles for food.

The largest and the most successful are the albatrosses, birds of the Roaring Forties and other stormy regions. These birds live in the wildest, windiest parts of the ocean, for they need strong wind in order to travel. It is quite usual for an albatross to operate thousands of miles from its home base. Swiftly it glides these vast distances, making use of the wind currents reflected upwards from the sloping sides of the great waves. The albatrosses have many smaller relatives – the petrels, shearwaters and diving petrels – which can also glide and fly great distances without tiring.

The penguins, perhaps the most primitive group of sea-birds, lost their power of flight millions of years ago, for they have specialised in swimming at tremendous speeds under water. Only one of the world's fifteen species of penguin reaches the equator: all the rest are confined to the southern hemisphere, breeding on cool coasts and islands, and around the Antarctic continent, where there are few or no beasts of prey to destroy them at their nesting beaches.

Another successful order of sea-birds includes the pelicans, the gannets, the cormorants, the tropicbirds and the frigate-birds. The gannets and pelicans soar well and dive upon their fish-prey from a great height. Cormorants fly rather heavily but swim well under water, using both feet and wings. Tropic-birds can catch flying-fish in the air, and frigate-birds, perhaps the most agile and swift of all the sea-birds, soar magnificently on broad wings and often get their food by pursuing other sea-birds and compelling them to disgorge.

By no means all of the world's forty-two species of gulls are sea-birds and only two – the kittiwakes – can be truly called birds of the open ocean. But the smaller and closely related terns include many kinds which make long journeys by sea, feeding by diving from a height on to the small animals near the surface of the sea.

The auks, found in the world's more northerly seas, all use their wings for swimming under water as well as flying in the air. The name penguin was first given not to the true penguin but to the one member of the auk family which had become flightless. The great auk lived in the North Atlantic, a far more dangerous place for a flightless sea-bird than the southern home of the penguins. Its last island sanctuaries were all discovered by hungry seamen, and the last great auks were killed in Iceland in 1844.

Yet in the open oceans, where sea-birds seek their food and fortunes, there are very few other creatures (except perhaps man) to prey on them. The albatrosses and the bigger penguins not only take several years to reach maturity but only have one young at a time; and some breed only every other year. Nobody yet knows for certain how long these great birds of the ocean can live – but it may well be as long as a man, and perhaps even longer.

Greatest of all sea-birds, the wandering albat
with wing-span of over eleven feet, displays in court
on the cold, southern island of South Geor
Inspired by photograph by Niall R

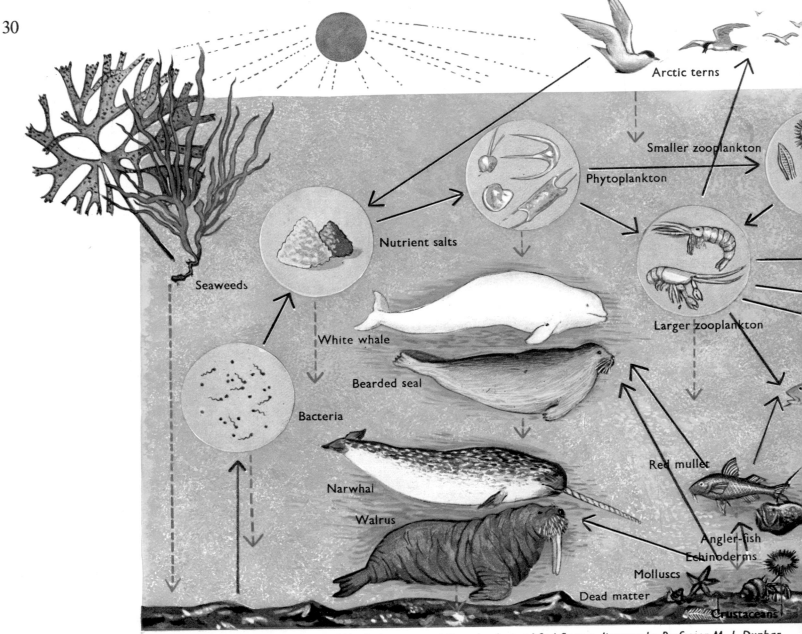

The pattern of life in the polar seas of North America and Greenland, simplified from a diagram by Professor M. J. Dunbar.

In some ways the pattern of life in the sea can be likened to a pyramid, with comparatively few (and generally large) animals of prey at the top, and masses of tiny plant organisms at the bottom.

The little green plants of the sea-surface, which scientists call phytoplankton, can (with the aid of sunlight) turn the sea's salts into living matter. They do not look like grass, but they fill much the same place in nature, and are grazed upon by the tiny animals of the sea, called zooplankton.

The word 'plankton' is used to describe all creatures which are carried hither and thither by the sea's currents. The larger animals of the zoo-plankton include many shrimp-like creatures, well over an inch long, which eat the smaller plankton animals. These shrimps are in turn eaten by all sorts of larger creatures, from fishes to the largest animals in the world, the toothless whales. The mouths of these whales contain a huge array of 'whalebone' strips (they are not really made of bone, but of a horny substance called baleen) with which they sift their food out of the water as they swim slowly through the plankton shoals with their mouths open. Some whales, of course, also eat fish, as do the seals.

Large fish eat small fish. In the Arctic regions of the New World the bottom fish are preyed upon by the Greenland shark, several kinds of toothed whales, and the bearded seal. The killer whale also eats seals whenever he gets the chance,

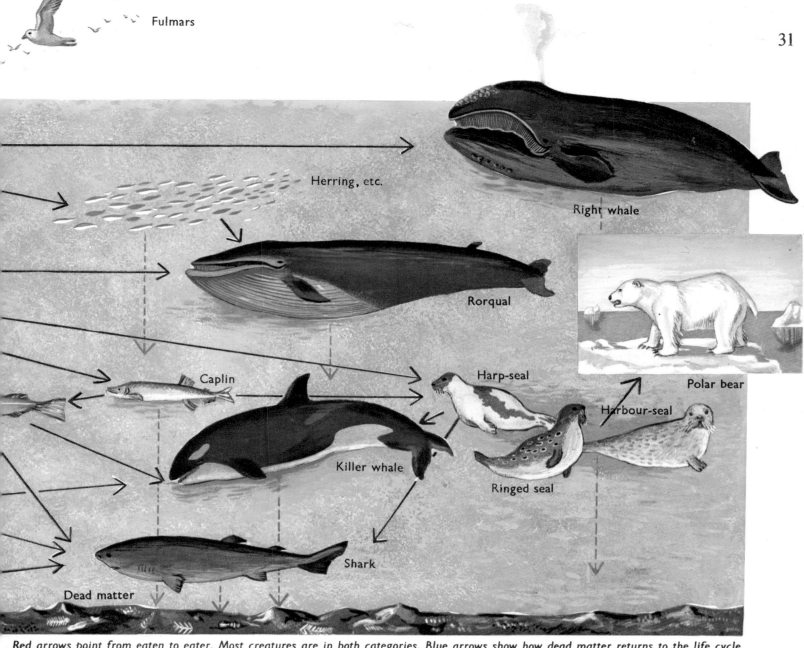

Red arrows point from eaten to eater. Most creatures are in both categories. Blue arrows show how dead matter returns to the life cycle.

and may even attack whales larger than himself.

The walrus prefers molluscs to fish. It brings up mussels and clams from the depths and crushes them in its powerful jaws.

When the animals and plants of the sea die, their remains drift to the bottom; there, by the work of bacteria and other natural agencies, they are turned once more into food for the scavenging animals of the sea-bottom, and into salts which again play their part in the cycle of life.

In some ways this great cycle is like an eternal continuous performance at the cinema; but each performance is slightly different, for there is no such thing as a true and absolute balance of nature. The members of a community of animals and plants are always having different fortunes. Some may gradually fail in competition with other creatures, and eventually become extinct. Others may become very successful and abundant. Yet others may change from one food to another, and modify their habits and behaviour; or even separate into two species, each with a different place in nature.

But despite change, each part of the sea contains its typical community of creatures, bound together by eating and being eaten. Scientists have only just begun to understand the complex pattern of marine life. Nature's network in the sea, and the way it is arranged and tied together is beginning to fascinate marine biologists even more than the individual plants and animals that belong to it.

The search for food brought early men to the sea's shore; but long years passed before they trusted their lives to its stormy surface.

The Sea Challenges Man

IN THE WEB OF LIFE described on the previous page there is one missing element – man. We could have put him in, for the community of animals that we described belongs to the Canadian Arctic or Greenland, and the Eskimo is a member of that community, who lives by preying upon several of the animals which form an essential part of it.

It is only very recently that man has come upon the scene, and has begun to accept the challenge of the sea. The living creatures of the sea, as we have described them, have taken millions of years to evolve. As a species, man has only existed for thousands: indeed, we can only begin to pick up his trail properly at the end of the last Ice Age, about twenty thousand years ago. What we now know about the most primitive men tells us that they were not unlike the Eskimo in their way of living. Like the Eskimo, the earliest men lived mainly (but not always) within range of the sea. Near the sea the land was usually most fertile, and the seashore itself was an important source of food.

Long before he domesticated animals and plants, man lived in little communities by the shore,

gathering seaweed, spearing fish, snaring birds, collecting mussels, limpets and other molluscs. To such men the sea was at once the source of existence and of danger. Men sheltered in terror from the unpredictable storms, but quickly learned the regular rhythm of the tides; for between tide-marks lived much of their food and from the edge of the sea came many of the raw materials from which they could make clothes, shelter, weapons and even ornaments. The beautiful charms, ornaments, masks and tools shown in the margin of this page are all made by people of today whose way of life is not unlike that of early men.

In many different parts of the world at different times, there came a day when the shore-living shellfish-eaters no longer looked fearfully and wonderingly at a distant shore across the sea, but boldly set out to explore it in some primitive log raft or dug-out canoe. Early man gained familiarity first with the seashore, then gradually, after many experiments and disasters, with the open seas. We know that his familiarity never bred contempt. For him the sea was, as it still is to many of us, a thing of mystery and magic, the giver of sustenance and the taker of life.

Seldom did he sail upon it without the invocation of magic, or prayer to such gods as he knew.

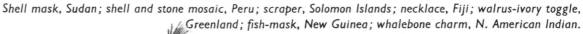

Shell mask, Sudan; shell and stone mosaic, Peru; scraper, Solomon Islands; necklace, Fiji; walrus-ivory toggle, Greenland; fish-mask, New Guinea; whalebone charm, N. American Indian.

Lowering a lead-line
from the stern of a Greek trireme.

Some of the world's first boat-builders at work, depicted on an ancient Egyptian tomb.

All sorts of boats were invented and developed in different parts of the early world. The ancient Egyptians of five thousand years ago made great boats by hollowing trees; but when we study the paintings on the tombs of Egyptian kings we find that they also made ships, and may well have been the first men to do so anywhere in the world. A ship, of course, is a boat so big that it cannot be hollowed from one trunk, but must be constructed piece by piece. Ship-building, therefore, involves much greater skills – in shaping and bracing wood and applying planks to each other so that a joint is waterproof. The earliest ships of the Egyptians were propelled not only by many oarsmen but also by the wind, for the mast-sail appears to have been invented at the same time as the ship.

The home of shipping, then, is in the Mediterranean Sea, and within it, in the three thousand years before the birth of Christ, there were many further developments. The Egyptians sailed their ships mainly along the great waterway of the Nile, and seldom ventured on long sea voyages. But in the twelfth century B.C. the Phoenicians, whose principal city was Tyre, brought ship-building and navigation to a fine art, traversing the length and breadth of the Mediterranean and carrying merchandise to and from most parts of the known world.

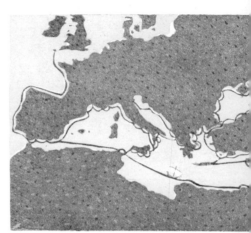

Phoenician and Greek mariners sailed the Mediterranean, sometimes reached Britain; but seldom ventured more than a few miles out of sight of land.

Solomon, king of Israel in the tenth century B.C., used the skilled navigators of his friend Hiram, king of Tyre, to pilot his fleet of great ships trading all over the Mediterranean, and bringing to Israel cargoes of 'gold, silver, ivory, apes and peacocks'. At the beginning of the seventh century B.C., it is said, a Phoenician fleet sailed out of the Mediterranean and right round Africa. The Phoenicians certainly traded as far as the tin mines of north-west Spain and south-west Britain.

Nobody now knows exactly what tricks of navigation the Phoenicians used, or what instruments they had. But we can be reasonably sure that, like all early seamen, they kept within sight of the coast as often as possible and that they had maps or charts showing the main coastal landmarks. They were also learned in astronomy, and when out of sight of land they certainly made use of the position of the sun or of star-clusters as navigational aids.

About four hundred years after the time of King Hiram, the Greeks gradually began to wrest sea supremacy from the Phoenicians, and we know that

Greek pilots sometimes located their position by taking samples of the deposits from the sea-bed. In shallow waters in the south-eastern Mediterranean they would drop a waxed lead-line overboard; if a certain kind of mud adhered to it, they knew they were within a few miles of the Nile delta.

The war-galleys of the ancient Mediterranean peoples were wooden ships, steered by one or more paddles, and propelled by scores of oarsmen. Some galleys were quinquiremes, with no less than five tiers of oars, but the typical fighting ship was a trireme, with three. In ships of this kind one of the decisive battles of the world was fought at Salamis, an island off Greece, in 480 B.C. The Greeks, greatly outnumbered by the Persians, destroyed the enemy fleet by superior tactics and seamanship. Removing their main-masts and all their sails, the swift Greek galleys rammed and sank, or boarded two hundred of the larger, clumsier Persian sailing vessels, for the loss of only forty of their own ships. Not for the only time in history, the fate of two great nations had been decided in a narrow strip of sea.

The Romans, builders of many early lighthouses, used fishes as a motif for mosaics, sea-snails for making a rich purple dye.

In the narrow seas near Salamis, Greek ships rammed and defeated two hundred of the larger, clumsier Persian vessels.

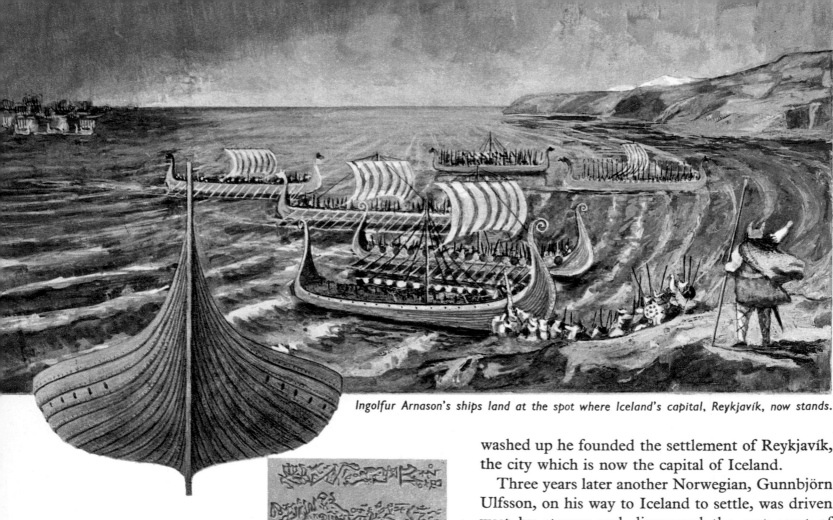

Ingolfur Arnason's ships land at the spot where Iceland's capital, Reykjavík, now stands.

Rune-stones – Viking relics – in America

The centuries which followed the collapse of the last great Mediterranean civilisation of antiquity are often described as the Dark Ages, in which man is supposed to have made little progress. This is hardly so, for during that time there was much exploration all over the world; and it was then that man ceased to be a rather timid point-to-point navigator of the coastal waters, and became master voyager of the open oceans. In the Pacific the greatest voyagers were the Polynesians; in the Atlantic, the Vikings.

Perhaps Iceland had already been discovered as early as 325 B.C.; for though the Greek navigator Pytheas probably never reached it from the Mediterranean, he was given directions to it by the Irish, so clear that many people think they may already have known the way there.

When the Vikings colonised Iceland in 874 A.D. they found Celtic people from Scotland and Ireland already living there. Ingolfur Arnason, the first great Norwegian noble to establish a home in Iceland, brought his door-posts with him on the voyage across the stormy sea. Within sight of Iceland he cast them adrift; and where they were

washed up he founded the settlement of Reykjavík, the city which is now the capital of Iceland.

Three years later another Norwegian, Gunnbjörn Ulfsson, on his way to Iceland to settle, was driven west by storms and discovered the east coast of Greenland. In 982, remembering Gunnbjörn's story of a new coast, the Icelander, Eric the Red, reached Greenland and founded on its south-west side the first European colony in the New World. About twenty years later his son, Lief, discovered America. From Greenland, he passed along the Labrador coast and reached Newfoundland; some historians think he may even have landed in New England.

Often the Vikings hunted the whale, by methods still used in the Faeroe Islands. But the great

During the Dark Ages, the Vikings became master voyagers of the open sea, sailing to Iceland, Greenland, Labrador and Newfoundland.

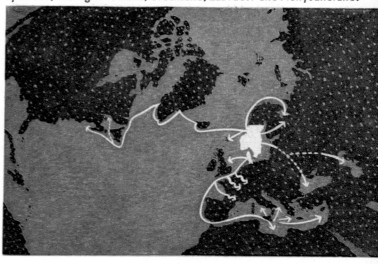

Basque coat of arms, showing early whale
hunt along the northern coasts of Spain.

Off the Faeroe Islands, men still hunt the caaing whale in much the same fashion.

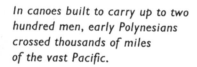

In canoes built to carry up to two
hundred men, early Polynesians
crossed thousands of miles
of the vast Pacific.

whalers of the later Dark Ages were the Basques,
who, from Spain, operated far into the Atlantic.

Nobody knows exactly when the brown-skinned
Polynesians first explored into the Pacific from their
home in Asia; it was probably not long after the
birth of Christ. Quite independently of Western
ship-builders, they became for a thousand years even
greater navigators than the Vikings, and voyagers of
incredible skill and daring. Their craft were funda-
mentally canoes, but canoes so modified that they
worked as well as ships, and could carry up to two
hundred men. For long voyages they often used a
huge double canoe, or catamaran, with a connecting
platform on which was built a deck-house. They
learned to navigate by the sun and by the stars, and
by studying the prevailing winds and swells of the
great ocean. From their base in Tahiti they made
voyages thousands of miles across landless sea to
Hawaii in the north and New Zealand in the south.

In the Dark Ages, then, a few brave and bold
men – Europeans and southern Asiatics – accepted
the frightening challenge of the open sea. They began
to see it almost as a second home, and to use it not
merely as a dangerous road from one known land to
another, but as an adventurous highway to the
unknown, the unpossessed and the unexploited.
Most of us think that the opening-up of the world
began with Christopher Columbus in 1492. Not a bit
of it. The round earth was discovered by the Vikings
and the Polynesians, the early explorers who
first crossed its greatest and most terrible oceans.

The maps of the Dark Ages gave no clue to the earth's real shape.
British Museum

Henry the Navigator, inspirer of sea-explorers

Columbus, greatest of all names in exploration.

Vasco da Gama discovered the eastern sea-route to India.

Magellan named the Pacific Ocean

The greatest surge of sea-exploration in history owed its beginnings to a Portuguese prince, Henry the Navigator, born near the close of the fourteenth century. Although he never went far to sea himself, he established the finest library of maps in the world and gathered around him brave captains, learned astronomers and skilled ship-builders.

By studying Prince Henry's collection of charts, a young Italian, Christopher Columbus, became convinced that if he sailed west from the Azores or the Canaries he would reach India. At that time geographers thought that the world's sphere was smaller than it really is, and had no idea that westward between Africa and India lay the vast continents of America. Columbus asked King John II of Portugal to back his expedition in search of a westward route to India, but at that time all the Portuguese explorers were trying to find a route round Africa. So he went to Spain where he eventually gained the support of Queen Isabella.

Late in 1492, thirty-three days out from the Canaries, Columbus sighted the Bahamas. 'The West Indies', he called them, for he believed that India lay not far beyond. Three times more Columbus made voyages of discovery to the New World, but he never found the wealth he had expected, or the route to India. In 1504 he returned to Spain, disappointed and oblivious of the fame that history was to bestow on him.

Meanwhile the Portuguese had found a route to India round Africa. In 1497 an expedition of four trading ships, under the command of Vasco da Gama, had finally reached Calicut in India after a very long voyage. When he got back to Lisbon, late in 1499, da Gama brought the first cargo of Indian spices ever to reach Europe by sea.

The Spaniards, Portugal's greatest maritime rivals, now saw that their opportunity lay in developing the western route to the Indies. Early in the sixteenth century they realised that the two American continents were continuous, and that only by rounding them to the south could they reach Asia. It was this southern route that Magellan sought when he sailed from Spain in 1519.

More than a year went by before Magellan, with his small fleet reduced from five ships to three, sailed through the straits now named after him. He called the ocean into which he had so laboriously made his way the Pacific. Magellan himself was never to return to Spain. In 1521 he was killed in a fight with Philippine islanders. But one of his officers, Sebastian del Cano, eventually returned round the Cape of Good Hope with a cargo of

Sixteenth-century maps gave recognisable outlines of Africa, Asia, Europe and the Americas.
British Museum

Sir Francis Drake, world navigator
and conqueror of the Armada

Vitus Jonassen
Bering

Abel Janszoon Tasman

Captain James Cook

spices, and reached Seville in 1522 – with only eighteen men. Del Cano's ship, the *Vittoria*, was the first ever to circumnavigate the globe.

With the rise of Sir Francis Drake, born about 1540, power in the new oceans of the world began to flow to Britain. Drake and many of the other great British captains of his period were in a sense no more than buccaneers, for the object of most of their voyages was to raid Spain's possessions in the New World and intercept and capture her ships. Drake made many raids on the Spanish Main, and between 1577 and 1580 he sailed right round the world in his famous ship, the *Golden Hind*, visiting what is now San Francisco, and returning home laden with spoil. In 1588 Drake finally broke the sea-power of Spain, when, in command of the English fleet, he destroyed the Spanish Armada which attempted to invade England.

During the next two centuries, seamen of many lands took part in discovering practically all the world's continents, countries and islands. In 1643 Tasman, a Dutchman, discovered Tasmania and western New Zealand; in 1741 Bering, a Dane in the service of Russia, discovered the narrow strait between Siberia and Alaska; and a few years later Captain Cook, an Englishman, discovered eastern New Zealand, eastern Australia and Hawaii. But it was the great sea-dogs of the fifteenth and sixteenth centuries who paved the way for all later sea-exploration, and it is of them we first think when we speak of 'The Age of Discovery'.

In the seventeenth century, William Dampier combined
the roles of pirate, explorer and geographer.

40 The European explorers of the sea were sometimes – like Captain Cook – in search of no more than adventure and scientific information. But adventurers and explorers could not have raised the money for their expeditions had not governments and private companies seen new opportunities of increasing power and wealth by overseas trade.

Wherever the explorer blazed his trail, bartering posts were established and trading ports quickly grew up. Traders soon realised that to keep a monopoly of a profitable trade, they often had to assume power. The trading ships of the rival European nations were often armed against piracy, against the over-enthusiasm of their rivals – and sometimes, even, against the governments of the people with whom they traded. The simple drive for trade developed into a struggle for overseas territories, and from the seventeenth century onwards many of the nations of Europe were periodically at war with each other in the process of empire-building. Trading posts became colonies; and colonies became associations of independently-minded peoples, with ideas of their own. By the twentieth century, most of the great colonies had

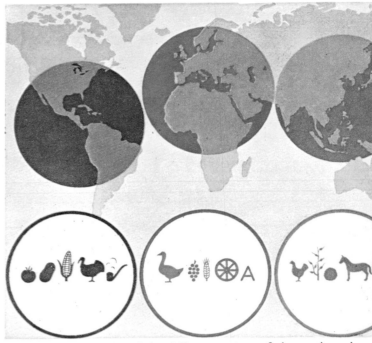

In early times, peoples of the different regions of the earth each used native plants and animals, each made special inventions.

become independent nations: many others still live under the flag of the mother country, as equal members in a family of nations.

As the first great transoceanic empires were built up the sea trade of the world grew to a scale never before known. Nations separated by thousands of miles of ocean came to depend on each other for many of the luxuries, refinements and even the necessities of life; and when political ties between mother country and colony were severed,

By 1800, ships from all parts of the world mingled in such great ports as Bombay.

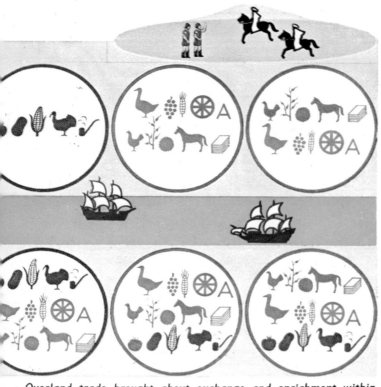

Immigrants from Britain sought opportunities in Australia, half a world from home.

Overland trade brought about exchange and enrichment within the Old World. Sea trade completed the process for the whole earth.

A sixteenth-century European trading post in Asia, forerunner of the famous East India Company.

interdependence often remained as strong as ever. Typical of the whole history of modern overseas trade, is the story of Bombay. Founded as a trading colony by the earliest Portuguese navigators to India, it was ceded to Britain in 1661, and developed by the famous East India Company. By the end of the eighteenth century, it was a hive of trading activity, alive with busy shipping. In 1950 Bombay became part of a great Asiatic republic, but its trade with Britain continues almost unchanged.

Early traders of the Hudson's Bay Company helped to found the great Dominion of Canada.

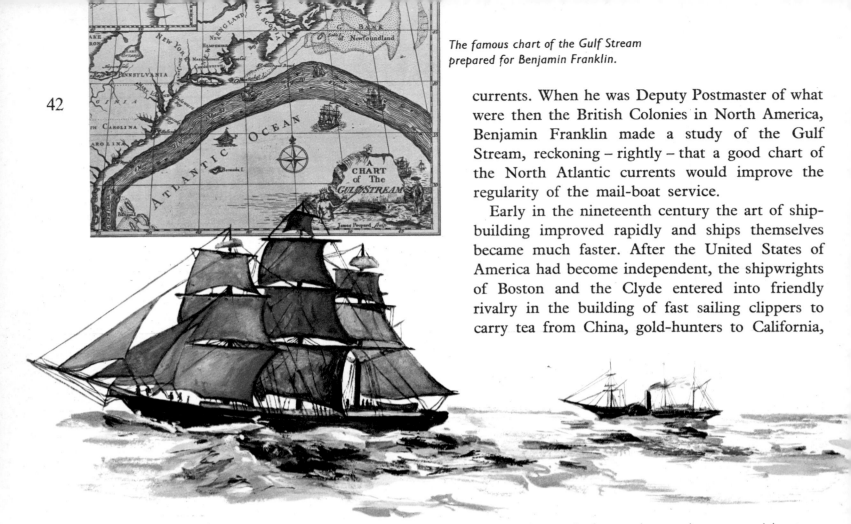

The famous chart of the Gulf Stream prepared for Benjamin Franklin.

currents. When he was Deputy Postmaster of what were then the British Colonies in North America, Benjamin Franklin made a study of the Gulf Stream, reckoning – rightly – that a good chart of the North Atlantic currents would improve the regularity of the mail-boat service.

Early in the nineteenth century the art of ship-building improved rapidly and ships themselves became much faster. After the United States of America had become independent, the shipwrights of Boston and the Clyde entered into friendly rivalry in the building of fast sailing clippers to carry tea from China, gold-hunters to California,

In the early nineteenth century, fast clipper-ships could sail almost contemptuously past the first cumbersome boats powered by steam.

Two hundred years ago the skill of seamen, the enterprise of explorers and the tenacity of traders had completely changed the ways of the world. Almost every great nation now owed its prosperity and power to ocean shipping. The sea could no longer remain the playground of buccaneers; it had to be made a safe, swift highway for ships.

In the effort to speed up the delivery of cargoes, seamen had long since learned to take advantage of the great prevailing winds of the ocean. Now a few men of science turned their attention to ocean-

Illustrated London News
The engine room of the 19,000-ton Great Eastern, launched in 1858.

wool from Australia, or fish from Newfoundland. One famous American-built clipper, the *Lightning*, is said to have sailed 436 miles in a day, an average speed of 18 knots – as good as that of many modern liners; in 1866 three small tea-clippers left Foochow at the same time and all arrived in London within a few hours of each other, ninety-nine days later.

Meanwhile steam, the great rival of sail, was making headway at sea. The first successful ship powered with a steam engine was built in 1802, but it took nearly a century for steamers to out-number sailing ships; for under full sail, even in light tropical winds, the clipper-ships sailed almost contemptuously past the early steamers. But the steam-vessel had one big advantage: largely inde-pendent of the wind, it could keep much more closely to a fixed time-table.

Ships first crossed the Atlantic by steam in 1835, and five years later a regular steamship service was instituted. With the invention of the compound steam engine, ships of the 1860's began to make non-stop runs of over eight thousand miles, and when the Suez Canal was opened in 1869, steam-ships, more manoeuvrable than sailing ships, really

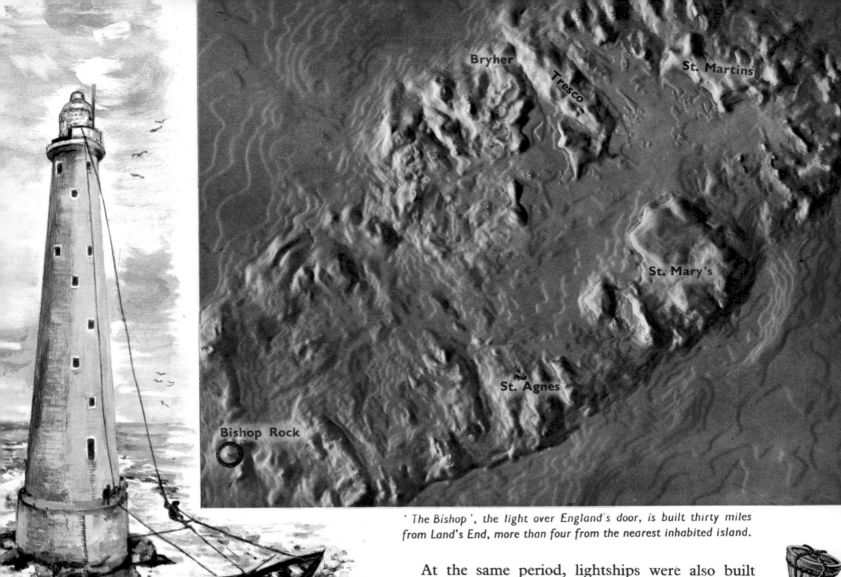

Bishop Rock Lighthouse : changing the crew.

' The Bishop ', the light over England's door, is built thirty miles from Land's End, more than four from the nearest inhabited island.

came into their own. By 1900 about 85 per cent of sea-borne goods were carried in steamers.

As the volume of traffic increased along the world's shipping lanes, the nations, often by mutual agreement, created new aids to safety. Lighthouses existed here and there in the Mediterranean before the birth of Christ, but in the nineteenth century they were built on the danger spots of all the coasts of the world, from the Straits of Malacca to the English Channel, from Alaska to Cape Horn. Marking, as they do, the most perilous spots, lighthouses had to be built where it was most difficult to build them. Work on the Bishop Rock, one of the most exposed of rock-lighthouses, was begun in 1847; in 1850 the first tower was swept away, and work had to begin again the next year. Not until 1858 did the first light shine.

At the same period, lightships were also built and anchored near dangerous reefs and shoals. Markers and beacons were designed to guide ships into difficult channels and ports. Lifeboat services grew up in many lands. Seamen coined a new international language of flags and light signals. Laws were adopted to control the over-loading of ships and the comfort of crews. Charts, made by the navies and surveying services of the principal nations, were widely published and made freely available to all the seamen of the world.

Early buoys of wicker

Lifeboat of over a century ago

Entering port, ship keeps line on guiding lights marking fairway.

Seventeenth-century Brighthelmstone – a simple coast village.
Picture Post Library

The elegant pastime
of shell-collecting

Nineteenth-century Brighton – established as a fashionable seaside resort.

As an interlude to the story of the sea, we must tell a short story of the shore. Perhaps the new return to the edge of the sea, which has now become the holiday habit of millions, began with the doctors of the seventeenth and eighteenth centuries, who advised the leisured classes about the curative properties of sea-water, and were really the first to start the cult of sea-bathing.

We think little now of running down to a sandy beach for a quick dip; but two hundred years ago, and even in the early years of our own century, bathing was a complicated, fussy business. The bather had to undress in a hut on wheels; and a horse pulled his bathing machine axle-deep into the sea to ensure his privacy as he took the plunge. On royal occasions the ritual was still more complicated, even if rather less private: in July, 1789, George III's bathing machine was pulled out into the sea off Weymouth sands, on the south coast of England; and the moment the monarch stepped into the water a band struck up the National Anthem.

It was George III's eldest son, the Prince Regent, who set the seal of fashion on the seaside habit in Britain. Towards the close of the eighteenth century he built a pavilion at Brighton, spent much of his time there, and collected around him many of the leaders of a fashionable and slightly raffish society. The town, which not long before had been a quiet fishing village, suddenly developed into a gay and bustling watering-place. During the first half of the nineteenth century many other coastal towns in

various parts of Europe and America began to bustle in the same kind of way, too.

In the old days, men had built seaside towns with their backs to the sea to cheat the wet winds: now came the age of the front, the promenade, and the pier; the era of donkey rides, ice-cream, deck-chairs, concert-parties, seaside landladies and what the butler saw. Shell-collecting became an accomplishment as necessary to the elegant young woman as an ability to play upon the pianoforte. Eminent naturalists, like Philip Gosse, approached seashore life more scientifically and wrote books on the plants and animals of the zone between the tides. Captain Matthew Webb took bathing seriously... and swam the Channel. Using a powerful breast-stroke, and assisted by nothing but the encouragement of a few friends in small boats, he left Dover on 24th August, 1875, and splashed ashore at

King George III bathes, while a band standing thigh-deep in the sea plays the National Anthem. From an engraving by John Nixon.

The seaside cult spread quickly.   The beach at Trouville, in Normandy, was crowded with bathers and sand-castle builders eighty years ago.

Disasters such as the sinking of the Birkenhead were reminders that beyond pier and promenade the open sea remained untamed.

Calais on the following day, twenty-one and three-quarter hours after entering the water.

So strong did the seaside movement become a hundred years ago that the beach-haunters – at least many of them – had begun to forget how cruel and unpredictable the sea could be; how little, with all their new ideas, they had progressed towards taming it.

The competition between sail and steam was then at its height. Sailors took heavy risks to run their ships to schedule, and the safety devices at their disposal were quite crude in comparison with those available today. Now and then a trim clipper or a clumsy paddle-steamer would leave port and disappear, never to be heard of again. A complete list of the sea tragedies of a century ago would be a long and sad one, but we can give a few examples of the disasters that shook the complacency of the age.

In 1852 the *Birkenhead*, carrying cavalry and infantry to South Africa, split in two on a reef. Of its complement of 638 souls, 446 were lost. In 1854, the *Arctic* was sunk in a collision off the coast of Newfoundland, and 323 were lost out of 368; and in the same year the *City of Glasgow* and the *Lady Nugent* disappeared with all hands – over eight hundred and seventy all told.

Beyond the gay lights of pier and promenade the open sea was then, as it still can be now, a fearful, almost untameable, enemy. For centuries men had fought it with incredible courage and great skill, but a stronger weapon than either was still needed.

46 Man can master nothing that he does not understand. By the work of devoted scientists who have sought to understand the sea, we have at last begun to make it, if not our friend, at least our ally.

The age of sea-scientists really began when Captain James Cook sailed forth in the *Endeavour* on his first voyage in August, 1768. Cook took an astronomer with him, and a biologist too; and his expeditions returned not only with charts, but with all sorts of scientific information about the sea and the creatures that live in it. Since that time, the survey of the sea has occupied the minds of some of the finest ships' captains and greatest scientists the world has known.

In 1799, for instance, the famous German scientist and writer, Alexander von Humboldt, sailed from Europe to South America in the *Pizarro*. One of the earliest true geographers of the sea, he discovered the great current, now named after him, which carries cool water from the southern oceans northwards along the west coast of South America.

Between December, 1831, and October, 1836, the world's greatest naturalist studied at sea. Charles Darwin, as civilian scientist to H.M.S. *Beagle*, a surveying vessel under the command of Captain FitzRoy, sailed round the world, and on his voyage collected with passionate zeal all kinds of natural history specimens, particularly rocks, plants and animals. Working at his material and notes in his

An early microscope

Forbes used a dredge to explore nature under Manx coastal seas.

Humboldt studied currents on the western coast of South America.

Working in his cabin on H.M.S. Beagle, Darwin first guessed that all life might be descended from one or a few common ancestors.

A century ago, lead-lines were man's only contact with the deeps.

cramped cabin-laboratory on the small wooden ship, he laid the foundations of the theory of evolution, and learned much about the nature of the sea.

While Darwin was visiting remote islands in the Atlantic and the Pacific, another young man, Edward Forbes, was busy dredging specimens of marine life round the shores of his native land, the Isle of Man. Forbes died before he was forty, and his most important work, *The Natural History of the European Seas*, was not published until five years after his death. It was to become a foundation-stone of our present scientific knowledge of the creatures that live in the sea.

Naturalists had been dredging creatures from the bottom of the shallow seas ever since the Norwegian scientist, Otho Frederick Müller, invented a dredge-bag with an iron-frame mouth for the purpose in 1750; but not even Forbes, who brought dredging to a fine art, knew the great depth at which life could exist. Indeed, this was scarcely imagined until deep-sea dredging began with the voyages of H.M.S. *Porcupine*, on which the scientific work was supervised by another fine naturalist, C. Wyville Thomson. The haul-up of the first really deep dredge on 22nd July, 1869, must have been an exciting moment. That day, the apparatus of the *Porcupine* brought up many living creatures from a depth of no less than 2435 fathoms. Thomson was the first man to prove conclusively that primitive forms of life exist at great depths. His successors have carried dredging far deeper, and have proved that even the higher forms of fish exist in extraordinary variety in the abyss of the ocean. But it will be many years before scientists complete the pictures in the great mosaic of deep-sea life that Thomson first began to piece together.

In July, 1869, the Porcupine made dredgings which first proved that life exists at great depths.

Man Challenges The Sea

IF WE ARE TO NAME A YEAR in which man truly began to return the challenge of the sea, we must choose 1872, when a surveying ship of the British Royal Navy, H.M.S. *Challenger*, began a three-year voyage with Wyville Thomson as chief scientist.

Already man knew that life ran deep in the sea. In 1818 Sir John Ross's expedition to Baffin Bay found a starfish entangled in a sounding-line from 800 fathoms. In 1858 Fleeming Jenkin, examining a cable dredged up for repair from over one thousand fathoms in the Mediterranean, had found several animals attached to it. Thomson, as we know, had later found evidence of life much deeper. Now, during a cruise of 69,000 miles, the *Challenger* added more to man's knowledge of the sea than the sum of all he had learned before.

Many islands and rocks, previously badly charted, were fixed by exact determinations of their true positions; remote and little-known parts of the oceans were fully surveyed; and magnificent collections were made of the marine life within them. Scientists determined the temperature of sea-water at different depths; found that below a hundred fathoms this temperature is quite independent of the seasons; and discovered that over large areas of the ocean's bottom temperatures are quite constant. For the first time a picture of the depths and contours of the great ocean basins, true in broad outline, emerged. Perhaps most important of all, scientists determined the nature, extent and direction of the world's principal ocean currents.

The *Challenger's* badge, showing a knight casting down a gauntlet before the waves, symbolised only the beginning of man's challenge to the sea. Within the next few years ships of many nations were continuing the work – among them the German vessel, S.M.S. *Gazelle*, which made a long voyage in the South Pacific, South Atlantic and Indian Oceans, and the U.S.S. *Tuscarora*, which sounded the North Pacific to aid the laying of a cable.

A broken cable, raised,
reveals life at 1,000 fathoms.

H.M.S. Challenger was des
solely for scientific sea-explor

U.S. Navy pilot charts still carry the words : Founded upon the researches made . . . by Matthew Fontaine Maury.
U.S. Department of Hydrography

Listening to sound-waves reflected from sea-floor. Time of travel indicates the depth of water.

The states of the world began to take responsibility for the charting of the seas quite early. The Dutch first issued government charts in the middle of the seventeenth century. In 1713, the Board of Longitude was set up in Britain, and a prize of £20,000 was offered to anybody who could devise a reliable method of calculating longitude at sea. By 1720 France had its own Chart Office. In 1795 the Hydrographic Department of the British Royal Navy was formally established.

In the days of sail, deep-sea soundings were seldom reliable. Ships were apt to drift while their

French and Italian surveys began this chart in the 1850's. Many soundings taken since then by several nations have contributed detail.

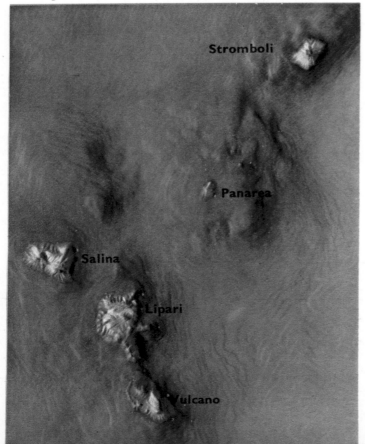

Stromboli

Panarea

Salina

Lipari

Vulcano

lead-lines were lowered, and the length of line between ship and sea-bed was not, therefore, a true measurement of the depth of the water. The nineteenth-century steamship, which could use its engines to counteract drifting, made far more accurate soundings. Until the early 1870's soundings were made slowly and laboriously with miles of bulky, hempen rope, lowered by hand; after the invention of Lord Kelvin's sounding device, they were made far more quickly and easily with fine piano-wire, lowered by means of a winch.

Aided by new inventions and a new spirit of scientific enquiry, the surveyors of the mid-nineteenth century were no longer content to chart coast-lines and the contours under the sea; they also explored such problems as magnetism and the salinity and temperatures of the water.

In 1855 Lieutenant M. F. Maury, of the United States Navy, brought out the first text-book of oceanography, and compiled charts of the winds and currents of the world's oceans. These new aids enabled English ship-masters to cut their average sailing time to Australia from 124 to 97 days, and New York captains to reduce their passage to California round Cape Horn from 183 to 135 days. No wonder Maury later became an admiral! In 1857 the British Admiralty first began to issue regular daily notices to mariners, bringing charts into line with new discoveries as quickly as possible; and the first Admiralty chart showing curves of constant magnetic variation over the North Atlantic Ocean was published two years later.

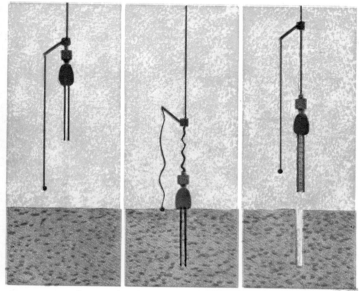

As core-sampler touches bottom, weight drives tube deep into ooze.

Reversing bottles are lowered at intervals on a wire. A weight is released and strikes first bottle; this reverses, sending another weight down to the next. Each bottle collects a sample of water at the moment of reversal.

Another forward stride in the charting of the oceans came between the two world wars, when the German research ship *Meteor* made a most thorough survey of the whole of the Atlantic. The scientists of the *Meteor* were interested in many things – in the distribution of plankton, in ocean currents, and in sea-water temperatures. But they contributed most originally and effectively to our knowledge of soundings, for the *Meteor* was the first important surveying ship to be equipped with a new device: an echo-sounder. Sound waves emitted from the ship were timed on their journey to the ocean floor (from which they were reflected) and back. As the ship slowly sailed or drifted, a continuous profile of the sea-floor could be recorded; and ever since the days of the *Meteor's* great voyage ships have netted the oceans with a cross-work of echo-sounding lines, from which the under-sea contours have been reconstructed in precise detail.

The job of the modern hydrographer is complex. He must sound the entire water area that he has been allotted, record the positions of all shelves, reefs, rocks and submerged wrecks, and of breakers, tide-rips, eddies, weed-beds, fishing-stakes and buoys. At frequent and regular intervals he must take samples of the sea-bottom. He must compile clear sailing directions for ports and channels, note the height and shapes of all land features useful in coast-recognition, accurately fix high and low water marks, measure tidal streams and currents, observe magnetic variations both ashore and afloat, determine true meridians by precise astronomical observations. Furthermore, he must make continuous weather notes and collect samples of the water and of the living creatures of the sea.

New devices are constantly being introduced to help the hydrographer's work. The piston core-sampler can bring him samples of sea-bed oozes and muds from a depth of fifty feet below the sea. Ingenious self-recording reversing bottles enable him to sample the water, and work out its circulation and temperature far below the surface of the ocean. Clever under-water current recorders have been devised; and a machine has even been invented which can take a continuous sample of planktonic life as it is towed through the sea at a set depth. Bottles and plastic envelopes are released in the ocean, advertising (in several languages) rewards to finders, who, by stating the time and place of recovery, are sending vital information about the speed and direction of surface currents.

Though no international charts are yet published, conventional surveying is still carried on by all the principal maritime nations, who exchange information freely – and freely share in the benefits of new inventions, irrespective of the country of origin.

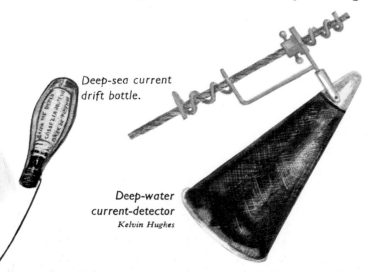

Deep-sea current drift bottle.

Drift envelope

Deep-water current-detector
Kelvin Hughes

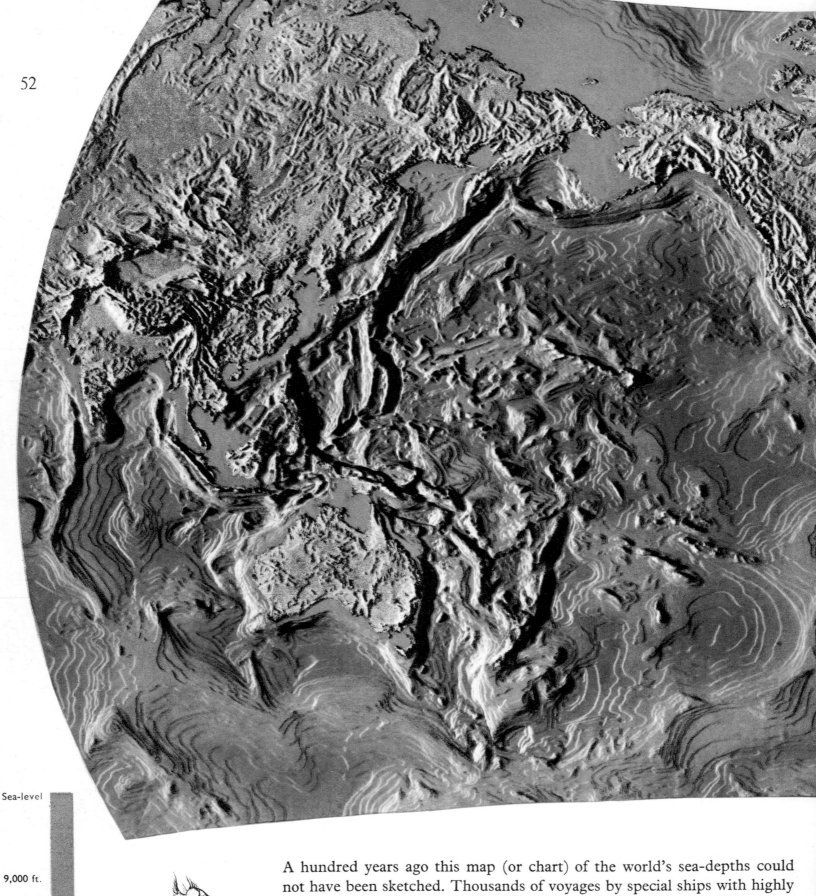

Sea-level

9,000 ft.

15,000 ft.

30,000 ft.

A hundred years ago this map (or chart) of the world's sea-depths could not have been sketched. Thousands of voyages by special ships with highly trained crews have produced the information on which it is based. Piece by piece the sea-going nations have explored and sounded first their own coasts; next, the coasts of their dependencies; and last (but far from least), the depths of the world's great oceans. In peace and war, surveying ships revise and recheck their mapping. Nation has exchanged information with nation, so that all may understand the seas, and sail safely upon them.

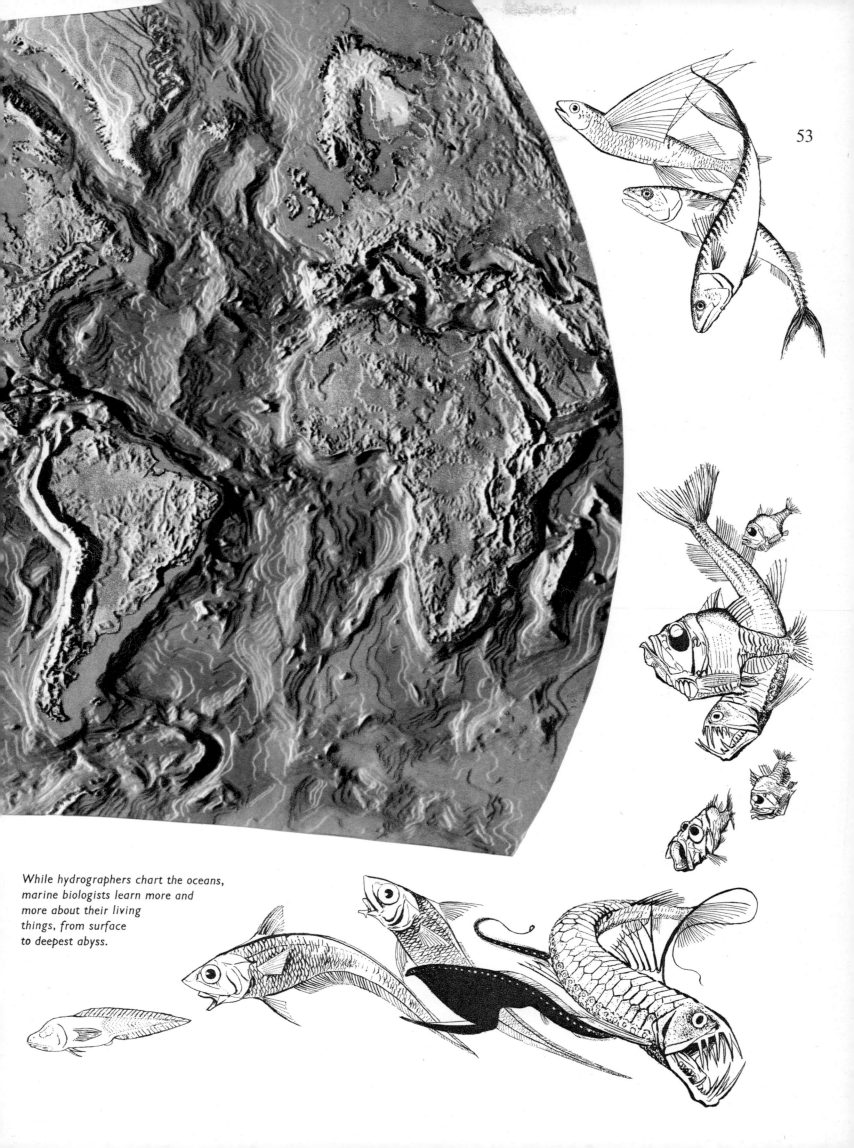

While hydrographers chart the oceans, marine biologists learn more and more about their living things, from surface to deepest abyss.

54

*Prince Albert of Monaco,
a pioneer oceanographer . . .*

and founder of Monaco's magnificent marine biological research station, museum and aquarium.
From Founders of Oceanography, *Sir William Herdman, publ. Edward Arnold*

For years the great exploring ships carried marine scientists with them, whose collections accumulated in the museums of the capital cities and universities of the civilised world. Soon institutes devoted entirely to oceanography and marine biology began to spring up on the coasts. From the earliest days these had their own libraries, laboratories, museums and aquaria; often, too, they had their own ships.

An ichthyologist dissects an interesting species of Pacific fish.
Scripps Institution of Oceanography

The first marine biological station was founded at Naples, in Italy, by the great German zoologist, Anton Dohrn; and scientists from all countries work there to this day, freely exchanging specimens and ideas. In Britain the most important research station is at Plymouth, where the Marine Biological Association founded an Institute in 1884. There are many other stations in the British Isles, and fine laboratories staffed by able scientists in Holland, Germany, France, Italy and Scandinavia.

The largest marine biological laboratory in the world is at Woods Hole, in Massachusetts. There are, too, a dozen or more institutions on the coast of the North American continent now devoted generally to oceanography. The oldest of them – and the largest such unit in the world – is the Scripps Institution of Oceanography at San Diego, in California. Of its five research vessels, the flagship has ranged as far as Peru, the Marshall Islands and the Gulf of Alaska.

Many great stations for sea-science were founded first as shore bases for ships. Indeed, we could truthfully say that the first marine biological stations were themselves ships, such as the little boat in which Edward Forbes investigated the waters around the Isle of Man, and the famous yacht *Princesse Alice* in which Prince Albert of Monaco explored the seas for many years. In 1910,

The sea-water hall in the great aquarium of the Zoological Society of London. whose collection is used for both research and education.

Prince Albert opened the magnificent aquarium, museum and laboratory on the shores of his Mediterranean principality.

With the rise of oceanographic institutes and marine biological stations came, too, the building of great aquaria for educational purposes. There is none in Europe more well-designed than that of the Zoological Society in London. First completed in 1924, the London Zoo's Aquarium shows a vast collection of living sea and fresh water fish from areas as wide apart as the Indian Ocean and the cold waters of the Arctic circle. Millions of people have enjoyed there their only glimpse of the rarer and more interesting creatures of the deep, perhaps scarcely realising the organisation required to provide each creature with its proper food, water and temperature.

Many of the marine biological stations of the world are connected not only with universities and museums but with governments; and much of their research is devoted to the improvement of fisheries. From their surveys come ideas for the exploitation of new fishing grounds, or new kinds of fish. They give expert advice on the many questions which arise from over-fishing, make suggestions for the conservation of spawning grounds, and provide the fisherman with much of the intelligence upon which the world's greatest food industry depends.

Blue bands and lines round coasts show main commercial fisheries of the world. Scientific research and new enterprise may change this map out of all recognition during the next hundred years.

From Grimsby, on England's east coast, trawlers operate as far as Labrador, Greenland, Spitsbergen, landing 200,000 tons of fish each year.

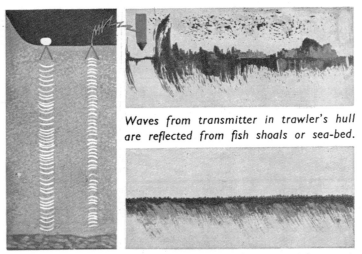

Waves from transmitter in trawler's hull are reflected from fish shoals or sea-bed.

Echoes, traced on moving paper band, show (top) coal-fish in mid-water, dense herring-shoal below; (bottom) smooth sea-bed, no fish.

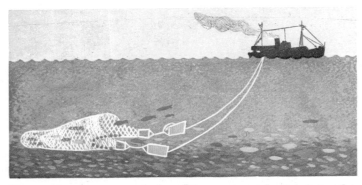

The trawl: an open-mouthed net that scoops up bottom-living fish.

The drift-net: a hanging trap that entangles herring near surface.

We can begin to realise the tremendous importance of the fishing industry when we know that everybody in the North American continent – man, woman and child – eats an average of over forty pounds of fish a year. In Japan, Malaya, Sweden, Portugal, Britain and Iceland, the amount is even larger, and in Norway it is roughly three times as great.

When the world's population was smaller, the demand for fish could be met by line-fishing, seine-netting and small-scale trawling, but in the modern world the fisherman must use more efficient methods. The story of modern sea-harvesting began in 1837 when North Sea fishing-boats first towed really large trawl nets, with mouths held open by otter-boards, over the sea-bed. Within twenty years trawlers began to carry ice, which meant that they could stay at sea for some time and store their catches; some were already powered by steam, which helped to extend their range of operations.

Today the most important method of fishing apart from trawling – at least in Western Europe – is drifting. Drifters fish the herring, one of the most nutritious animals in the world, a fish which can be smoked, salted or preserved in other ways so that it can reach people far inland in good condition.

All sorts of modern devices aid our farmers of the sea. Echo-sounders have been devised which can not only detect shoals of fish below the surface, but also the depth at which they swim, and even, in some cases, what sort of fish they are. Advances in refrigeration have made it possible to store huge catches at sea; and some ships are also fitted with machinery for converting fish-waste into cattle food, and for extracting and processing cod-liver oil. One of Russia's most important exports is the flesh of the great spider-crab of the western Pacific; and in the

Russian crab-fishers taking their catch to a floating cannery.

Before harpooning, whale-catcher spots its prey by echo-sounding.

Sea of Okhotsk busy crab-boats feed mother ships which are themselves large floating canneries.

But man has learned by bitter experience that the stocks of sea-creatures he can catch are not infinite; that as he improves his methods, so must he control the place, time and quantity of his fishing.

From 1610 onwards, the Dutch led the other great sea-nations of Western Europe in a race to exploit the whales of Spitsbergen, Greenland and the edge of the Arctic ice-pack. Until 1780 up to three hundred and fifty whaling-vessels visited Greenland every year. In the nineteenth century the whale-fishing of the north came to an end, not from the want of human enterprise, but because nearly all the whales had been killed off. The giant whaling factory ships of today, and the fast harpoon vessels that feed them, operate only near the Antarctic, the last area where whales survive in numbers.

Kelvin Hughes

A blue whale is 'flensed' (cut up for oil, meat and bones) on the deck of a modern factory ship. Beyond, a catcher brings in more whales.

The maiden voyage of the 'unsinkable' Titanic ends in disaster.

When a trawler sets out for the Arctic Ocean, or a whaling expedition for the Antarctic, there are hazards of storm to be faced, hardships of biting cold to be endured, now as in the past. But at least the seafaring man of today knows that his ship is as safe as modern science and humane legislation can make it; and even in the remotest waters he is in constant touch with the shore and, with other ships. Not very long ago the greatest liners could scarcely boast such security.

In the spring of 1912, the 66,000-ton White Star liner *Titanic* set out on her first voyage from Southampton to New York. The largest liner afloat, and equipped with sixteen water-tight compartments, she was thought to be unsinkable. Although she carried passengers and crew to the number of 2,207, there were boats for only 1,178. Throughout the voyage there was no boat-drill.

Just before midnight on 14th April, in a calm sea and under a moonless sky, she struck an iceberg some distance south of Newfoundland. Mortally gashed in her starboard side, the 'unsinkable' *Titanic* remained afloat for nearly three hours; but when her voyage ended, in the most dangerous iceberg area of the Atlantic, 1502 souls were lost.

The *Titanic's* radio operator, who was eventually drowned, sent out distress signals until the rising

On every liner of today, radio men keep a twenty-four-hour watch.

Patrol boats watch for — and destroy — icebergs off Newfoundland.

*From her lonely ocean station,
H.M.S. Weather Explorer releases
a meteorological balloon.*

water reached his transmitter. Fifty-eight miles away these were received by the *Carpathia*, which rescued 705 survivors from the boats, having reached the scene of the disaster, at full speed, over an hour after the great liner had gone down. Less than ten miles away, the *California* had been unable to do anything, because her sole radio operator had gone to bed and had not heard the call for help.

The coming of wireless had saved lives at sea as long ago as 1899, but in 1912 there was still a lot to learn about sea-safety – as, indeed, there still is. As a direct result of the *Titanic* disaster, regulations were made that a twenty-four-hour radio service should be maintained on all liners; the rules for the construction of water-tight compartments were improved; and an iceberg patrol service was started in the western North Atlantic, internationally maintained, but manned primarily by the U.S. Coastguard Service. An international convention for the safety of life at sea was held in London just before the first World War.

Today, sea-safety is being sought in many new ways. Weather ships, belonging to the principal sea-going nations of the North Atlantic, and in constant radio contact with meteorological stations on shore, relieve each other at set positions in the open ocean, so that a permanent watch can be kept. The predictions of the world's meteorological services become more precise year by year. Gales and storms, as they move about the Atlantic, can be followed, and their future movements and changes predicted, for the benefit of ships – often to the nearest hour. Lifeboat and coastguard services, assisted by radio and radar, make rescue prompt; and the new arm of aviation plays its part in the saving of life at sea. To the helicopter, in particular, often goes the task of plucking sick or ship-wrecked men from the waves, or from a tilting deck.

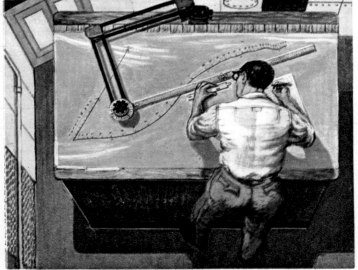

Weather men constantly gather information, predict track of storms.

Air-sea rescue helicopters pick casualties from ships at sea.

Calmly, officers of a cross-Channel packet navigate through fog.

Without incident of any kind, and scarcely behind schedule, their ship enters the harbour, at Dover.

Radar guides aircraft to floating runway.

A thousand years ago men navigated only by the sun, the stars and other signs of nature. Like the birds and other wild animals, which do the same, they were often lost. But, slowly at first, man invented for himself new devices for finding direction, measuring speed, and determining position.

It seems likely, though it is not certain, that the magnetic compass was first used by Arab seamen in the twelfth century. Early ships' compasses consisted of needles either mounted on pivots or floating on sticks in little baths of water. Today's magnetic compass is a far more refined instrument but, like its early counterpart, it points true north and south in only a few parts of the world. A newer and even more accurate tool is the gyro-compass, in which the position of the needle depends on the rotation of the earth, and which always points due north and south.

The early navigators knew that to find latitude they must measure the angle between sun and horizon; but the notched sticks and similar crude devices they used seldom gave accurate results. Not until 1731, when John Hadley invented the optical sextant, was it possible to determine latitude with comparative ease and near accuracy.

Left, radar scanner ; right, aerial for V.H.F. radio, at entrance to a modern port.

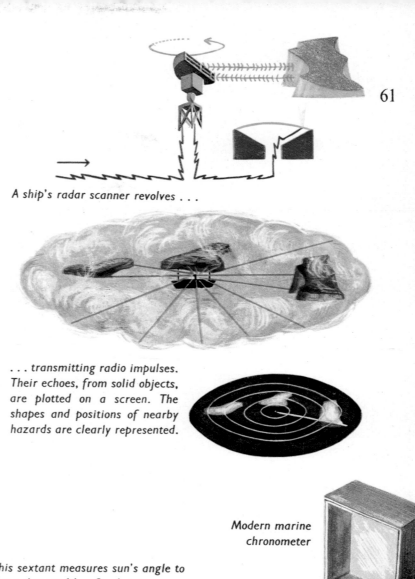

A ship's radar scanner revolves . . .

. . . transmitting radio impulses. Their echoes, from solid objects, are plotted on a screen. The shapes and positions of nearby hazards are clearly represented.

Officers fit radar-scan to chart, fix position with dead accuracy.

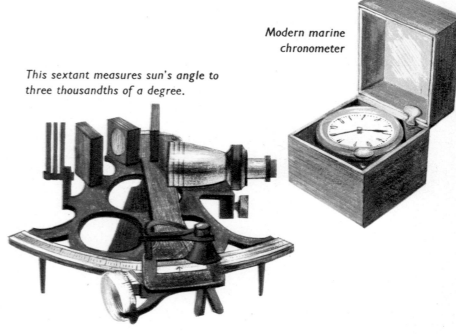

Modern marine chronometer

This sextant measures sun's angle to three thousandths of a degree.

Captain Cook carried an improved version of Hadley's sextant on his famous voyages, and it was that and the chronometer which enabled him to fix accurately the positions of distant shores and islands. For to determine longitude as well as latitude, a navigator needs both chronometer and sextant. A chronometer is no more than a clock which will go true and unchecked for months at a time. John Harrison's marine chronometer was perfected just in time for Cook to carry one with him on his second voyage, in 1772. It was less than eight minutes slow after three years at sea.

In the old days, a seaman measured the progress of his ship through the water by heaving the log – a piece of weighted, floating wood attached to a line marked with evenly-spaced knots. By counting the number of knots which passed the ship in a given time, he could estimate his speed with surprising accuracy. The latest equivalent of the old log is an instrument attached to the ship's hull, which, from the passage of water through a tube, produces a record of speed and distance travelled.

For twenty-nine years after Marconi applied for his first patent, in 1896, ships used radio only for communication; but in 1925 direct radio-navigation also came into use. Today radio beams from transmitters round the world's coasts enable ships to pick up their positions on direction-finding receivers. In 1922 Marconi foresaw an even more accurate method of radio-navigation, for he suggested the possibility of designing apparatus to transmit radio waves and to detect their echoes, reflected from distant surfaces.

Echo-radio, or radar, was quickly developed, and today, on their radar-scanners, ships' navigators can identify the outlines of coasts, of nearby vessels and other hazards. In foggy seas, ships can travel in safety at scarcely reduced speed.

In 1897, Turbinia roared past a fleet of warships at 34½ knots.

The finest navigational instruments are of little use in an unseaworthy ship. The ship-builders' inventions, through the years, have brought revolutions in the design of vessels just as exciting and important as those of compass, chronometer and radar.

Ships have sailed the seas by power generated within them for a century and a half. Novelties such as the screw-propeller and the steam-condenser soon put steamers on level terms with the fastest sailing clippers. A hundred years ago some steamships were already very large and could put up a fine performance. The American *Adriatic* of 1856, for instance, was a ship of nearly 6,000 tons, whose great paddles could drive her across the Atlantic at a speed of 13½ knots. But most steam-powered ships of the period used a huge quantity of coal, and used it quite uneconomically. Steam was generated, passed into a single cylinder and then pushed out of the exhaust with only a fraction of its energy used. In 1854 an engine was devised in which exhaust steam was passed into a second cylinder and made to do more work; and twenty years later came a further advance – the first three-cylinder, or triple-expansion, engines.

S.S. United States, the fastest passenger liner now afloat, under construction in a dry dock at Newport News, Virginia, U.S.A., in 1950.

A remarkable new development in naval engineering was brought dramatically to the public notice in 1897. Britain was celebrating the sixtieth anniversary of Queen Victoria's accession to the throne, and at Spithead, near the Isle of Wight, a great fleet of warships was anchored, dressed overall for the special occasion. Suddenly a small low craft roared into view at what was then the fantastic speed of 34½ knots. The *Turbinia*, designed by Charles Parsons, was one of the first vessels in the world to use steam turbines in place of steam-cylinders. Within a few years many great liners were equipped with these revolutionary engines.

Soon ships began to burn oil instead of coal to raise steam; and with the invention of the internal combustion engine some ships became independent of steam altogether. It is fifty years since the first motor-driven vessel crossed the Atlantic, and many liners built during the past quarter of a century are driven by Diesel engines.

Perhaps we can best appreciate the progress of powered shipping if we follow the speed and size of some famous transatlantic liners of recent times. For some early years of this century the Blue Riband of the Atlantic was held by a succession of fine German liners. Then, in 1910, it fell to the famous British Cunard liner *Mauretania*, which cruised at 25 knots, had a tonnage of nearly 32,000, and held the Atlantic record for twenty-two years. The 46,000-ton German liners *Bremen* and *Europa* wrested the record from the *Mauretania* in 1929 and 1930 at a speed of 26½ knots. In the 1940's the famous 'Queens', both at over 80,000 tons, brought the record back to Britain at over 30 knots.

The fastest passenger vessel now afloat is the American steamship *United States*. On her maiden voyage in 1952 she sailed from the Ambrose Light to the Bishop Rock in three days, ten hours, forty minutes, an average speed of 35.6 knots, breaking the record with some ease and gaining the Blue Riband of the Atlantic for the U.S.A.

Today over a quarter of the world's shipping is built in Great Britain and Northern Ireland. In one recent year two hundred and twenty ships were built there, with a total gross tonnage of 1,317,463. In the same year Germany built even more ships (two hundred and forty-four) but with a rather smaller total tonnage (818,221).

Other nations of ship-builders who produced about half a million tons in that year were Japan, the United States of America and Sweden; and many other maritime countries added their quota of fine new vessels to the world's grand total.

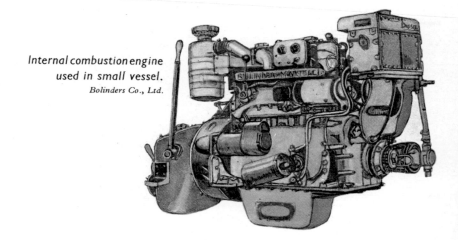

Internal combustion engine used in small vessel.
Bolinders Co., Ltd.

Ballast-tanks, bulkheads and other spaces

Refrigerators and cold stores

Crew accommodation, recreation, washrooms, etc.

General storage space

Machinery, plotting, wireless, control rooms

H.M.S. Vidal, Britain's most modern surveying ship, was completed at Chatham in 1954. A diesel vessel of 2,000 tons, with all the latest electronic devices for surveying, she carries her own helicopter, surveying launches, printing press.

Seaweed on a Hebridean shore – a source of valuable alginates.

Purifying iodine from sea-deposit.

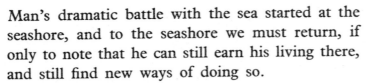

Magnesia derived from sea-water in a settling tank in north-east England. Part of the process for the extraction of an abundant and valuable metal.

Man's dramatic battle with the sea started at the seashore, and to the seashore we must return, if only to note that he can still earn his living there, and still find new ways of doing so.

Long before the dawn of history man gathered molluscs on the shore; in those times the shell-fish harvest must often have been a matter of life and death. Today men still gather sea-food, for oysters and clams, mussels and abalones find a ready sale in the gastronomic markets of the world's big cities. Oyster men farm their oysters in many parts of the world with a careful husbandry, scientifically caring for the spawning beds on which their business depends. The U.S.A., Britain and New Zealand all have their famous oyster beds; but the main areas of oyster cultivation at present are in France and Japan. In the nineteenth century, the French appetite for oysters increased so fast that the oyster beds began to give out, and the government had to control the amount of fishing.

One of the oldest forms of seashore commerce is the extraction of salt. As a business it is not so old as fishing, but it is certainly older than the fish-trade, for without salt no fisherman of ancient times could preserve his catch long enough to sell it in distant markets. There is evidence that the Chinese were extracting salt from the sea more than four thousand years ago, and to this day the salt harvest is won around the shores of warmer countries with the aid of the sun. India alone produces a million and a half tons of salt every year from the sea, by feeding the tide into vast pans on the sun-baked coastal flats, and allowing the water to evaporate. In Palestine the waters of the Dead Sea contain large amounts of potash, a mineral even more valuable than common salt, and of great use as a fertiliser. In the Dead Sea salt-pans most of the common salt is removed by a first evaporation and the potash is dried out in a second, in different pans.

Magnesium, lightest of the metals, is of tremendous importance in the aircraft industry and in the production of alloys and electric batteries. It is a metal by no means easy to win from the dry land; yet there is so much of it in the sea that if man extracted a hundred million tons every year for a million years he would reduce the magnesium content of sea-water only from 0.13 to 0.12 per cent. Now that a cheap method has been found for extracting magnesium from the sea, this useful metal can play its full part in man's economy. In the processes used in America and Britain, the

Salt is extracted from sea-water by the Indian sun, near Bombay.

Digging potash from an evaporation pan near the Dead Sea shore.

magnesium salt, after treatment with lime, forms magnesia which settles in great tanks. From the magnesia, the metal magnesium is afterwards extracted by a chemical and an electrical process.

From earliest times, coastal farmers have gathered seaweed and spread it on their lands to fertilise them. In many parts of Asia seaweed has been a human food from time immemorial, and in some northern islands it has been, and still is, a valuable natural food of sheep. For some centuries seaweeds have been burned to extract their salts, or treated to extract their valuable jelly. Today anybody who uses toothpaste or an absorbable medical dressing, or anybody who eats sausages, jellies, ice-cream or lemon-curd, is likely to be using or eating something which contains one of the alginates derived from seaweed. The alginate industry began after 1883, when this essential constituent of seaweeds was discovered. The world production is now estimated at more than three thousand tons.

Another valuable substance in seaweed is the element iodine. Nobody now attempts to extract this directly from seaweed; but in the coastal deserts of Chile there are large natural deposits of sea salt, on shores (now raised above the sea) which once grew great mats of seaweed. From the Chilean salt deposits iodine is extracted by a chemical process and purified by heating strongly for several days in large cement-lined retorts.

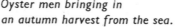

*Oyster men bringing in
an autumn harvest from the sea.*

The Panama Canal, swift highway between two great oceans, revolutionised the commerce of the Americas, speeded the trade of all the world.

Man has learned to take what the sea can give, and to travel everywhere upon it – sometimes under it. He has learned another thing besides: how to trim and change the sea's very shape to fit his needs.

In November, 1869, the first sea-going vessels began to pass through the Suez Canal. This great artery of world trade, a hundred miles long and completing a direct water route from the North Atlantic to the Indian Ocean, had taken ten years to cut through the desert sands of Egypt. As an idea, it was over a thousand years old: but the realisation of the idea was the result of the indefatigable work of the great Frenchman, Ferdinand de Lesseps. In recent years over twelve thousand ships carrying some 90 million tons of goods have passed through the Suez Canal annually.

Another man-made ocean connection, and an even greater feat of engineering, now makes the Atlantic and Pacific oceans one across the forty-mile Isthmus of Panama. De Lesseps had tried, and failed, to build a Panama Canal in the 1880's, but eventually, in spite of a bad climate, difficult terrain, and the menace of yellow fever, the great waterway was completed in 1915. In 1953 over 36 million tons of merchandise were carried through it in 7,410 ship-transits.

There are ten other large ship canals in the world, though none so important as Suez and Panama. The greatest of them is the Kiel Canal, between the North and Baltic Seas, opened in 1895.

In the previous year a canal had been opened in England which changed the economy of its indus-

Dredging the unfinished Suez Canal, ninety years ago.

Building the canal which made Manchester, an inland town, Britain's third port.

Manchester Ship Canal Co

trial north. By the standards of the time, the Manchester Ship Canal scheme was a prodigiously expensive one, and the canal itself took nearly seven years to build. But within a year of its opening, a million tons of goods had passed through it, and now over 18 million tons do so annually, making Manchester Britain's third largest port.

In the Netherlands, the farmers of the low Rhine delta have fought for centuries against the North Sea, ever encroaching on their slowly-sinking lands. Time and again they have built new sea walls, regained and freshened the saltings piece by piece, only to see their work destroyed in yet another disastrous flood. As late as 1953 a great North Sea surge breached the main dykes in south-west Holland, flooding 400,000 acres of land.

The industrious Dutch now fight the sea with a plan and with all the resources of modern engineering and machinery. By 1932 they had already enclosed the Zuyder Zee. Between 1200 and 1956 they have reclaimed 300,000 acres of land from this shallow sea; in the not far distant future they will win another quarter of a million acres from it. Where waves once broke and godwits whickered over the mud-flats, green fields and fine farmhouses now stretch as far as the eye can see; and Holland is steadily building up a coastline unlikely to be breached again. Man is rapidly winning his age-old battle with the sea. He is now free to enjoy it.

Ships' sirens proclaim closing of Zuyder Zee Dyke, on May 28th, 1932.

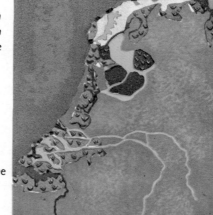

For hundreds of years the Dutch have fought to wrest land from the sea. This map shows how the battle is being won.

Land reclaimed long ago
Already won from Zuyder Zee
Future Z.Z. reclamations
—— Dykes still to be built
Other reclamations planned

Lush farmland, once part of the muddy bottom of the Zuyder Zee.

About a hundred and twenty-five miles off Dakar on the west coast of Africa the Atlantic Ocean's depth is about two and a half miles, or 13,280 feet. At about 1.30 p.m. on 15th February, 1954, the French naval engineer, Pierre Willm, saw this ocean-bottom through the porthole of the bathyscaphe, F.N.R.S.3. Quickly his companion, Lieutenant-Commander Georges Houot, in command of the bathyscaphe, took Willm's place at the porthole. 'I can see footprints,' he said. 'Tell me when you see the Abominable Merman,' said Willm.

Houot and Willm had reached by far the greatest depth from which any human being has returned alive; and, indeed, these daring pioneers had found the floor of the Atlantic covered with little cones and ridges, and with holes resembling footprints.

This was by no means the first adventure of living humans at great depths. As early as 1934, William Beebe and Otis Barton had reached 3,048 feet off Bermuda in a steel sphere, the bathysphere; and in 1949 Barton reached 4,500 feet off California in a similar sphere, the benthoscope. In 1953, Auguste Piccard and his son reached a depth of 10,392 feet in another bathyscaphe, the *Trieste*.

Who knows where these new and daring explorations will end? Someone already born may well see the world's greatest ocean depths, and bring back photographs of creatures unknown to science.

Already man has joyfully accepted the challenge of the sea's deep mysteries. With aqualungs, skin divers can stay below water as long as whales and far longer than seals. Under-water photography has, for the first time, brought to millions the beauties of sea life. Perhaps one day, not very far off, we shall have learned as much about fish as we know about birds. But we shall never learn the whole of the story of the sea's stormy surface or probe the last secret of the silent depths.

Yet perhaps the sea is really no different to us from what it was to Alcuin of York nearly twelve hundred years ago. One day, at the academy of Charlemagne, this sage had one of his many teacher's dialogues with Pepin, the Emperor's son.

'What is the sea?' asked Pepin.

Answered Alcuin: 'The path of the daring, the frontier of land, the decider of continents, the hostelry of rivers, the fountain of rain, a refuge in peril, a treat in pleasure.'